The Illustrated
Encyclopedia
of Animals
in Nature and Myth

The Illustrated Encyclopedia of Animals
in Nature and Myth

Fran Pickering

www.alligatorbooks.co.uk

© 2014 Alligator Books

Published by
Alligator Books
Gadd House, Arcadia Avenue
London N3 2JU

Written by Fran Pickering

Printed in China

Contents

LAND

About this book

W elcome to the exciting world of animals! This encyclopedia takes a different look at the animal kingdom. It explores how we live alongside animals and what makes them special to us. This book also explores the way in which we treat animals and why some have disappeared from our planet. By understanding how animals live, we can learn how we can protect them and their habitats.

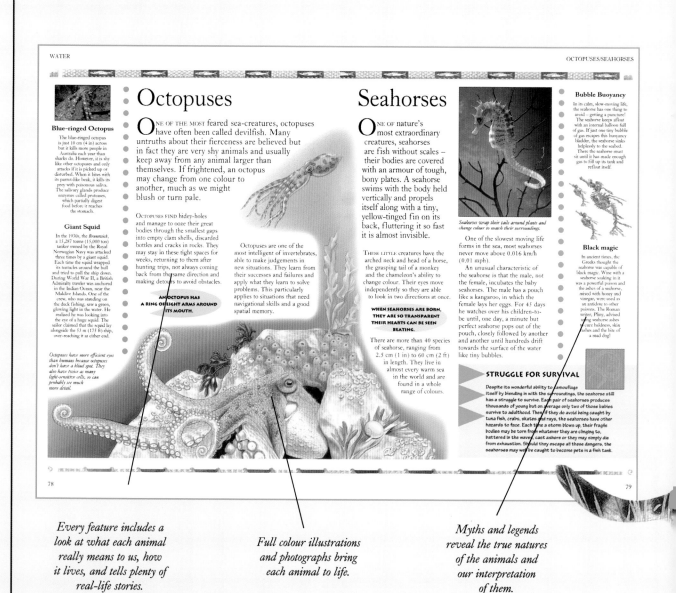

Octopuses

O NE OF THE MOST feared sea-creatures, octopuses have often been called devilfish. Many untruths about their fierceness are believed but in fact they are very shy animals and usually keep away from any animal larger than themselves. If frightened, an octopus may change from one colour to another, much as we might blush or turn pale.

OCTOPUSES FIND hidey-holes and manage to ooze their great bodies through the smallest gaps into empty clam shells, discarded bottles and cracks in rocks. They may stay in these tight spaces for weeks, returning to them after hunting trips, not always coming back from the same direction and making detours to avoid obstacles.

AN OCTOPUS HAS A RING OF EIGHT ARMS AROUND ITS MOUTH.

Octopuses have more efficient eyes than humans because octopuses don't have a blind spot. They also have twice as many light-sensitive cells, so can probably see much more detail.

Octopuses are one of the most intelligent of invertebrates, able to make judgements in new situations. They learn from their successes and failures and apply what they learn to solve problems. This particularly applies to situations that need navigational skills and a good spatial memory.

Blue-ringed Octopus

The blue-ringed octopus is just 10 cm (4 in) across but it kills more people in Australia each year than sharks do. However, it is shy like other octopuses and only attacks if it is picked up or disturbed. When it bites with its parrot-like beak, it kills its prey with poisonous saliva. The salivary glands produce enzymes called proteases, which partially digest food before it reaches the stomach.

Giant Squid

In the 1930s, the *Brunswick*, a 15,287 tonne (15,000 ton) tanker owned by the Royal Norwegian Navy was attacked three times by a giant squid. Each time the squid wrapped its tentacles around the hull and tried to pull the ship down. During World War II, a British Admiralty trawler was anchored in the Indian Ocean, near the Maldive Islands. One of the crew, who was standing on the deck fishing, saw a green, glowing light in the water. He realised he was looking into the eye of a huge squid. The sailor claimed that the squid lay alongside the 53 m (175 ft) ship, over-reaching it at either end.

Seahorses

O NE OF nature's most extraordinary creatures, seahorses are fish without scales – their bodies are covered with an armour of tough, bony plates. A seahorse swims with the body held vertically and propels itself along with a tiny, yellow-tinged fin on its back, fluttering it so fast it is almost invisible.

THESE LITTLE creatures have the arched neck and head of a horse, the grasping tail of a monkey and the chameleon's ability to change colour. Their eyes move independently so they are able to look in two directions at once.

WHEN SEAHORSES ARE BORN, THEY ARE SO TRANSPARENT THEIR HEARTS CAN BE SEEN BEATING.

There are more than 40 species of seahorse, ranging from 2.5 cm (1 in) to 60 cm (2 ft) in length. They live in almost every warm sea in the world and are found in a whole range of colours.

Seahorses wrap their tails around plants and change colour to match their surroundings.

One of the slowest moving life forms in the sea, most seahorses never move above 0.016 km/h (0.01 mph).

An unusual characteristic of the seahorse is that the male, not the female, incubates the baby seahorses. The male has a pouch like a kangaroo, in which the female lays her eggs. For 45 days he watches over his children-to-be until, one day, a minute but perfect seahorse pops out of the pouch, closely followed by another and another until hundreds drift towards the surface of the water like tiny bubbles.

Bubble Buoyancy

In its calm, slow-moving life, the seahorse has one thing to avoid – getting a puncture! The seahorse keeps afloat with an internal balloon full of gas. If just one tiny bubble of gas escapes this buoyancy bladder, the seahorse sinks helplessly to the seabed. There the seahorse must sit until it has made enough gas to fill up its tank and refloat itself.

Black magic

In ancient times, the Greeks thought the seahorse was capable of black magic. Wine with a seahorse soaking in it was a powerful poison and the ashes of a seahorse, mixed with honey and vinegar, were used as an antidote to other poisons. The Roman writer, Pliny, advised using seahorse ashes to cure baldness, skin rashes and the bite of a mad dog!

STRUGGLE FOR SURVIVAL

Despite its wonderful ability to camouflage itself by blending in with the surroundings, the seahorse still has a struggle to survive. Each pair of seahorses produces thousands of young but on average only two of those babies survive to adulthood. Then if they do avoid being caught by tuna fish, crabs, skates and rays, the seahorses have other hazards to face. Each time a storm blows up, their fragile bodies may be torn from whatever they are clinging to, battered in the waves, cast ashore or they may simply die from exhaustion. Should they escape all these dangers, the seahorses may well be caught to become pets in a fish tank.

78   79

Every feature includes a look at what each animal really means to us, how it lives, and tells plenty of real-life stories.

Full colour illustrations and photographs bring each animal to life.

Myths and legends reveal the true natures of the animals and our interpretation of them.

This book investigates the animals that live on the Earth in all their diversity. The encyclopedia is divided into six sections. The first section introduces the animal habitats of the world and the ways in which life is connected all over the planet. The next three sections explore the wide variety of land, air and water animals – from snakes and elephants, to whales and eagles.

The Myth section introduces animals from our imaginations – the creatures of legend and magic.

Finally, the last section focuses on unusual, extinct and endangered animal species.

Useful addresses

At the end of the encyclopedia you will find a list of useful addresses. These are designed to help you find out even more about your favourite animals and the part they play on our planet.

Glossary

Turn to page 128 for a list of more difficult and uncommon words.

Life on Earth

This is planet Earth as it is seen from space. It is the only planet in the solar system known to have life. Every day, we learn more and more about the ways in which our own lives are linked to the plants and animals which share the Earth with us. Since we depend on the planet for our very existence, it is important that we learn to respect and care for Earth to ensure that it is a safe and comfortable home for all the species which live on it in the future.

A habitat

A habitat is the natural home of a community of plants and animals. Each habitat has its own characteristic physical and chemical features, such as climate and soil type. If something from the habitat is destroyed, its structure is weakened.

An ecosystem

An ecosystem is a distinct area in the biosphere that is made up of living things. It contains rocks, soil, the surface of the ground and the air. Ecosystems are powered by energy from the Sun and they recycle materials such as the chemicals in plants. An ecosystem can be as large as a rainforest and desert or as small as a drop of rainwater.

Frogs

Frogs eat mostly small invertebrates but some will eat snails and rodents. They are the gardener's friends, eating bugs that damage plants. In turn they provide food for herons and other wading birds.

Fish

Different fish have different tastes. Some, for example, feed on plants while others feed on small animals such as insect larvae and tadpoles.

The web of life

If you use the Internet, you will know that part of it is called the World Wide Web – a network of computers across the whole world, which are linked together in electronic communities. In a similar way, the incredible variety of plants and animals on Earth are linked to one another but in ecological, rather than electronic, communities.

Heron

The heron eats mainly fish and small amphibians. It is at the top end of the web of pond and river life, eating the frogs that eat the insects around the pond or stream.

Dragonfly

The dragonfly is among the most ancient of living creatures, having been on Earth almost 300 million years. It is the tiger of the insect world, spending its days looking for different insects to catch and eat.

All the animals in this pond depend on plants or other animals for their food.

Animals at the top of a food chain have almost no predators except, sometimes, humans.

Water snails

Water snails are scavengers. They eat the debris, or rotting matter, at the bottom of the pond or river. In this way they help clean up the planet's waterways and recycle matter.

9

Animal habitats

Everyone needs somewhere to live. Wild animals make their homes in the forests, marshes, deserts, rivers and seas of our planet. Different regions of the world have different climates and this affects the planet's surface in those areas and the life that thrives there. Areas with different physical and chemical features, such as climate and soil type, are homes to different animals and are called habitats.

Tundra and polar

Each summer, the cold polar regions, with their oxygen-rich waters are home to many creatures. A variety of animals come and feed on the Arctic tundra or eat the fish and krill in the seas.

Deserts

On either side of the Equator, two bands of desert stretch across the Earth. The most obvious thing about a desert is the lack of water, and while the days can be burning hot, night temperatures can drop below freezing point.

North America

Atlantic Ocean

South America

Pacific Ocean

Marshes and swamps

Waterlogged places develop near lakes and rivers and along coastlines. They are usually home to small mammals, crocodiles, birds, fish, snakes and insects. Saltwater marshes and shores have habitats that change as the tides rise and fall.

Rainforests

A tropical forest only grows near the Equator, where the climate is hot and humid. These forests are home to the richest variety of wildlife that lives high in the treetops, or burrows in the dark of the decaying plants and leaves on the forest floor.

Forests and woodland

The world's coniferous forests and broad-leaved woodlands are home to many creatures that will have nowhere to go and nothing to eat if we continue to destroy their habitats for wood and land.

Rivers and lakes

Lakes and rivers are found all over the world. These freshwater habitats are home to thousands of different animals and fish.

Mountains

Every continent has mountainous regions. They contain a wide range of habitats including forests on the lower slopes, and grassland and tundra farther up. Mountains are home to many creatures, living at different heights.

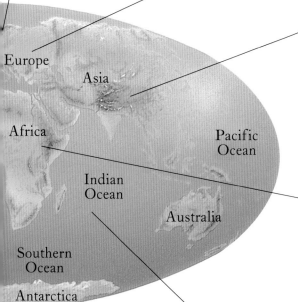

Europe

Asia

Africa

Pacific Ocean

Indian Ocean

Australia

Southern Ocean

Antarctica

Oceans

The ocean is a vast ecosystem, with deep underwater valleys and high mountains beneath the sea. It is home to millions of creatures, many of which we know little about. The oceans of the world help regulate the climate for all the other habitats.

Grasslands

All continents have areas of grasslands, where it is too dry for most trees to grow. Grasses provide a wonderful food supply as the whole plant can be eaten: the seeds, blades, stalk and roots.

Earth's creatures

We live amongst a vast range of different creatures, some of them living in habitats that humans cannot survive in, such as the air and the deep waters. Creatures are divided into different groups / categories, according to their body type. The scientific term for the whole range of life on Earth is biodiversity.

Toca toucan

Macaw

Caiman

Coati

Reptiles

Reptiles are vertebrates (animals with backbones) that depend the sun, heated earth and warm stones to keep them warm. They breathe air and have three-chambered hearts. Most reptiles, apart from some snakes and lizards, lay eggs.

Amazonian giant otters

Anaconda

Amazon kingfisher

Invertebrates

Invertebrates are animals without a backbone. About 97 percent of the world's species are invertebrates. They come in a vast range of body forms, from simple sponges to molluscs and insects.

Arapaima

Hatchet fish

Lungfish

Fish

Fish are vertebrates that live in water and have gills during their adult stage. Often they have limbs in the form of fins and propel themselves through water by moving their body from side to side.

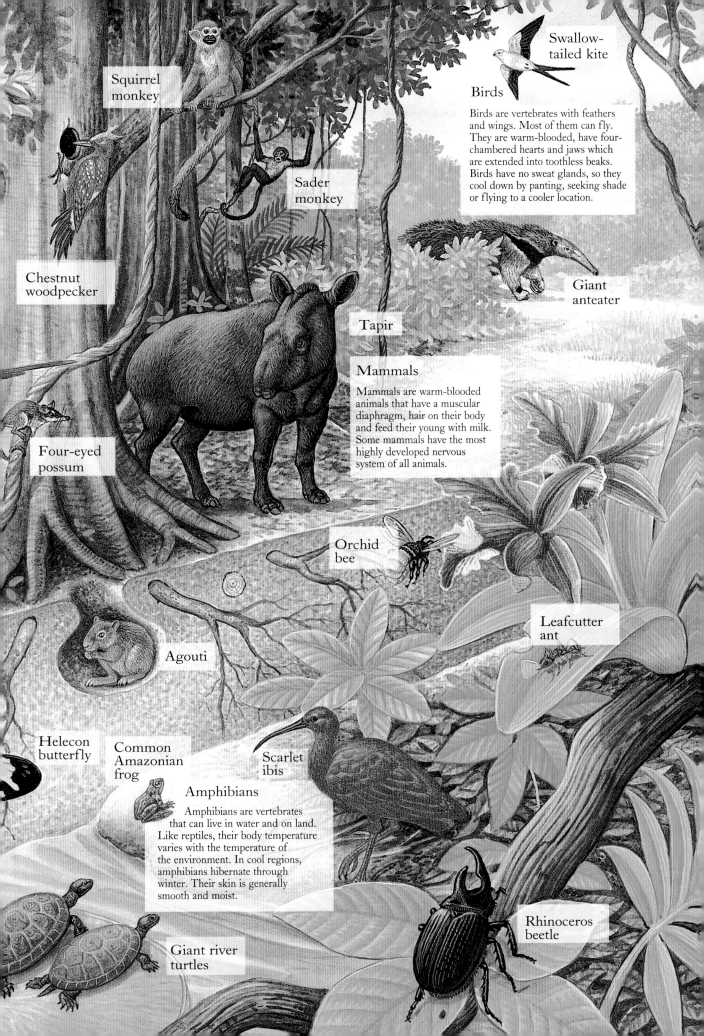

Squirrel
monkey

Swallow-
tailed kite

Birds

Birds are vertebrates with feathers
and wings. Most of them can fly.
They are warm-blooded, have four-
chambered hearts and jaws which
are extended into toothless beaks.
Birds have no sweat glands, so they
cool down by panting, seeking shade
or flying to a cooler location.

Sader
monkey

Chestnut
woodpecker

Giant
anteater

Tapir

Mammals

Mammals are warm-blooded
animals that have a muscular
diaphragm, hair on their body
and feed their young with milk.
Some mammals have the most
highly developed nervous
system of all animals.

Four-eyed
possum

Orchid
bee

Leafcutter
ant

Agouti

Helecon
butterfly

Common
Amazonian
frog

Scarlet
ibis

Amphibians

Amphibians are vertebrates
that can live in water and on land.
Like reptiles, their body temperature
varies with the temperature of
the environment. In cool regions,
amphibians hibernate through
winter. Their skin is generally
smooth and moist.

Giant river
turtles

Rhinoceros
beetle

Land

● ● ● ● ● ● ● ● ● ● ● ● ● ●

From the steamy rainforests around the Equator to the frozen tundra of the Arctic, the planet's landmasses offer a great diversity of habitats. Many animals, including humans, have adapted to the often-hostile environments and have survived harsh conditions to thrive on land. In this chapter we will explore these widely different habitats and the amazing abilities of the animals which make them home. The more we learn about different animal species, the more we are able to understand their importance and how we can help protect and preserve them.

SCIENTISTS BELIEVE ANIMALS FIRST MOVED FROM THE SEA TO THE LAND 400 MILLION YEARS AGO.

THERE ARE MORE THAN FOUR MILLION SPECIES ALIVE ON EARTH TODAY.

NO NEW ANIMAL HAS BEEN ADDED TO OUR DOMESTICATED LIVESTOCK FOR OVER 4000 YEARS.

Lions

Lions live in prides of between six and 20 lions. They are the most sociable animals of the cat family.

Heraldry

The lion has always been a prominent emblem in heraldry. This is probably because the nobility traditionally wanted to be associated with its image of royalty, bravery and strength. The lion is used on shields and coats of arms in 15 different postures. The most popular are: *rampant* (as in the picture above) standing erect on its hind legs, *passant gardant* as if walking in side view, its right paw raised, *sejant*, seated and *couchant*, lying down.

Jerome and the Lion

In AD 382, St Jerome became secretary to Pope Damascus. One day he was lecturing his disciples when a lion entered the schoolroom and lifted up its paw. All the disciples left in fear, but Jerome, seeing that the paw was wounded, pulled the thorn out. The grateful lion stayed with him as a pet, which is why St Jerome is always shown accompanied by a lion.

A lioness is pregnant for three and a half months. When her cubs arrive, other lionesses help to nurse the young.

F OR CENTURIES, THE LION has been known as the 'king of the beasts'. This may be because with its strength and confidence, it seems to have absolute control over everything in the animal kingdom; very few animals are able to even challenge a lion. The lion symbolises strength, nobility and courage.

THERE ARE FIVE KINDS of lion alive today: the Asian lion, which lives in the Gir Forest Reserve in northwest India, and four types of African lion. African lions are larger.

LION'S CAN CARRY TWICE THEIR OWN WEIGHT.

A mature African lion can stand 1.2 m (4 ft) high, measure over 3 m (10 ft) in length and weigh an average of 181 kg (400 lb) – about three times as much as a human being.

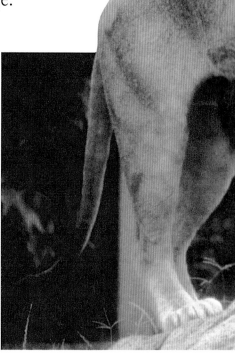

LIONS HUM WHEN HAPPY AND COUGH TO WARN SOMEONE OFF!

The stockier Asian lion has a smaller mane, a thicker coat with hairy elbows and a longer tail tassel.

Although lions may sit alone for hours, staring with regal aloofness into the distance, or dozing idly for 18-20 hours a day, they are not solitary by choice and need the support of a pride. In fact, they are the only members of the cat family to live in groups.

A lion can run 91 m (298 ft) in just four seconds and can bring down most prey on its own. However, it relies hugely on the lionesses. These females are marvellous examples of feline power. The lioness does most of the hunting to feed the pride, sometimes working on her own if the prey is small, such as a wart hog, or in a team with other lionesses when chasing buffalo or zebra. She is more active than the male and is more alert at all times.

**A LION'S ROAR
CAN BE HEARD 8 KM
(5 MILES) AWAY.**

The lioness is the real heart of the pride. The males may only last three years or so before younger males come to challenge them and take their place, but the females stay in the group.

Just like all cats, a lion has excellent eyesight and an intense, unblinking stare – a stare that reminds you that it is one of the most efficient natural killing machines on the planet.

Male lions form partnerships with other lions to defend the pride of female lions, with whom they breed. Usually these partnerships are with brothers or cousins reared in the same group. Between four and nine close male relatives may join forces. A solitary male will never join with more than one or two other males if they are non-relatives. This ensures that most of the cubs born to the pride belong to the same family, keeping the genetic line strong.

The Big Yawn

The lazy yawn of a sprawling lion may not be as harmless as it seems. The yawn speeds up the flow of blood through the lion's body, toning up its muscles and making an instant supply of energy available, which is needed by any lion just about to strike!

Lion Dances

In China, the New Year is celebrated with a lion dance to bring good luck. Five or more dancers make up the lion procession. One wears the mask head, one the body and the other three are musicians: a drummer, a gong player and a cymbalist. Lion colours have meanings: a black lion is a fighting lion, a red lion is full of happiness and prosperity and a multicoloured lion is the oldest and wisest.

Tiger Talk

A tiger has quite a range of sounds. It coughs to frighten animals away from a kill, moans in displeasure, barks to call to another tiger, hisses to blow insects off of a kill and roars in anger. One tiger seen stalking a wild buffalo was even heard to make a noise like a bull's bellow, perhaps to fool the buffalo into coming nearer!

The Java Sarong

Many years ago, on the island of Java, lived a magician who owned little pieces from a magic sarong. The material was yellow with black stripes and just big enough to wrap around his big toe. Once on the toe, the sarong stretched to cover the magician completely. As soon as this happened, he changed into a tiger, ready to go out and prowl through the forest.

Tigers

WILLIAM BLAKE, in his poem about tigers, described the animal as 'burning bright in the forest of the night'. Tigers are among the most magnificent of all the cats. They embody grace, beauty and power but are deadly killing machines. From the age of two years old, they live and hunt alone, masters of silent stalking and sudden ambush.

WHEN A TIGER IS IN its natural habitat, its black and orange markings match the patterns made by the Sun's rays or moonlight on grass and trees. It can creep silently from bush to bush or through the long grass without being seen, until close enough to leap on its prey. A tiger is at the top of its food chain – it is not at danger of being eaten by any animal. It prefers to eat hoofed animals, although it has been

THE INDIAN NAME FOR A TIGER IS 'SHER'.

known to catch birds, fish, crocodiles and even bears.

A tiger often attacks its prey from the side or from behind. Once within leaping range, a tiger breaks cover and jumps on to the back of the unsuspecting animal. It then wraps its mighty paws around the animal's throat.

The tiger then plunges its long teeth into the animal's neck, more often than not snapping the creature's spine. If the prey is not then dead, one bite to the throat finishes the job.

After a kill the tiger drags the animal's body out of sight and eats it. A tiger can devour up to 30 kg (66 lb) of meat at one time. Once it has eaten its fill, it covers the remains of the prey with leaves, returning to the carcass each night until it is finished.

**TIGERS CAN LIVE TO BE
BETWEEN 20-30 YEARS OLD.**

A tiger ambushes prey that comes to rivers to drink. It also enjoys lounging in water. However, this is when it is most vulnerable, so it often walks backwards into the water, keeping a careful lookout at the same time.

At the beginning of the 20th century, there were eight varieties of tiger. Now there are only five and probably little more than 5,000 tigers left on the planet. Of these, the Siberian tiger is the largest and one of the most endangered. From nose to tail, a Siberian tiger can measure

3-4 m (10-13 ft) and weighs on average up to 227 kg (500 lb). The heaviest tiger ever recorded was a male weighing 384 kg (847 lb). Only 20-30 South China tigers remain and these are living in wildlife reserves or zoos.

All tiger cubs stay with their mother until they are two years old, although some may stay until they are about five years old.

MAN-EATING TIGERS

Tigers usually have to be desperately hungry to eat people but some have been known to get a taste for human flesh and become man-eaters. The man-eating record is held by a tigress in Nepal in the early 1900s, who is supposed to have eaten 438 people in just eight years. One tigress killed 127 people in the province of Scindia, in India, frightening people from the main roads for months. In a single year, when records were kept in India, tigers killed 22,000 people and 80,000 domestic cattle. Some tiger experts claim that tigers only become man-eaters when wounded or crippled, or if they are a starving female with young to feed.

**THE BALI TIGER, THE
CASPIAN TIGER AND THE JAVA
TIGER ARE ALL EXTINCT.**

Although it is a sorry sight to see a caged tiger pacing back and forth, it is hoped that one day they may be able to live and breed in the wild again.

A tiger creeping through the long grass is well camouflaged.

Thai Tigers

A Thai myth tells that long ago, in a dense forest that once covered Thailand, there lived a huge animal with the body of an elephant and the head of a tiger. King Phan of Nakhon Pathom City ordered three brave hunters to catch the strange animal. When it was in captivity, the king bred a new race of war elephants. Villagers in Thailand still celebrate this myth once a year by making models of the tiger-headed elephant.

Bear Constellation

The bear has stirred people's imagination so much it has been given a place in the stars: Ursa Major - the Great Bear, and Ursa Minor - the Little Bear. One of the Greek myths tells the story of how the god Zeus fell in love with the nymph Callisto, and had a son called Arcas. His wife, the goddess Hera, was so jealous that she changed Callisto into a bear. To protect Callisto and Arcas from any further wrath, Zeus put them both into the sky as star constellations.

Medicine Woman

A Native American tale tells the story of the Bear Medicine Women. While she was still in the tomb, her father killed a bear. The spirit of the bear entered her body and she grew up to become the Bear Medicine Woman. The Bear Medicine ceremony is still celebrated in some parts of America, where people call for healing powers by imitating the actions of the bear.

Bears love the taste of fish and go into rivers during the summer to catch salmon as the fish head upstream.

Bears

IN ANCIENT LEGENDS, bears have been considered kin to humans. This may be because, like us, they can stand and walk on two legs. Bears are incredibly strong. In fact, no animal of equal size is more powerful. Despite their great size and strength, bears are usually gentle and good-natured and do not often seek out trouble. However, they have quick tempers and, if annoyed, their mood can change from playful to angry with little warning.

THERE ARE NINE different types of bear and they can be found in all parts of the world except Australia, Africa and Antarctica. The largest bear is the Alaskan brown bear, which stands 3-3.4 m (10-11 ft) high and the smallest is the sun bear which lives in Southern Asia. It is only about 1.2 m (4 ft) tall.

Bears eat berries, nuts, roots, insects, fish and any small animals they happen to catch. Their special skill is fishing, where they stand in rapids and hook out fish with their long, sharp claws. Bears also love honey and often raid wild or cultivated beehives. They rarely

forget where they have found food and will travel up to 97 km (60 mi) to a past site.

Female bears are wonderful mothers and keep their young with them for two to seven years. The females provide food for their cubs, as bear cubs do not fish on their own until they are around two years old. For these first years, they sit on the bank and watch their mother, learning the tricks of her trade. She-bears are very protective of their young and even the largest male tends to avoid females with cubs, even though males are likely to weigh twice as much as the females.

BEARS SLAP THE GROUND AND WOOF WHEN THEY ARE ABOUT TO ATTACK.

BLACK BEARS CAN RUN AS FAST AS SOME HORSES.

All bears are astonishingly swift. The black bear can reach running speeds of 56-64 km/h (35-40 mph) over short distances, which makes it a fierce predator.

Probably the most well-known bear is the grizzly, named for its 'grizzled' coat, not because it moans a lot! The grizzly bear can be any colour, from honey to almost black, but its hairs are tipped with white or silver.

Some bears, such as the Asian and American black bears, conserve energy by hibernating.

BRIGHT BEAR

In 1993, a Russian tourist agent was asked to take some American visitors on a wild bear hunt. Desperate to please his clients, the agent bought a bear from a Russian circus and released it into Moscow's Perdelkino Forest. The bear, not used to being loose, wandered around aimlessly while the American party closed in on him, ready to shoot. Meanwhile, a postman cycling through the forest bumped into the bear. Surprised and a little bit scared, the postman fell off his bike and ran off. The bear, remembering his circus days, picked up the bicycle and cycled off to safety, leaving the American tourists wandering around the forest for hours!

At the first sign of winter, when food becomes scarce, they find themselves a cave, tree or pile of leaves and drift off into a deep sleep until spring.

FIVE SPECIES OF BEARS ARE ON THE ENDANGERED ANIMAL LIST.

Forest Rescue

In 1997, a three-year old girl became lost in a forest in the USA. After three days and two nights, a search party was surprised to find the girl alive and well, asleep under a tree. The girl claimed that while lost she had met a bear with two cubs. She spent the day playing with the cubs and, when night fell, the she-bear licked the cubs and the girl. Then all four curled up together and fell asleep.

Dancing Bears

In parts of Asia and Europe, bears are made to dance on the streets to entertain tourists. Wild baby bears are taken from their mothers, forced to stand upright and taught to 'dance' on hot metal trays that burn their feet. A dancing bear is controlled by the pain caused when a chain pulls on a ring inserted through the palate between its mouth and nostrils.

The bear makes a grim enemy when it rears up on its hind legs in an aggressive stance; but it can be playful, too, and sometimes whizzes down snow-covered slopes in winter.

White Elephant

The term 'white elephant' is used to refer to something costly but useless. In Thailand all the white elephants belong to the king by law. Stories tell of kings who gave a white elephant to courtiers they wished to ruin. The elephant required expensive attention but, being royal, could not be put to work to earn its keep!

Elephant Graveyards

It is a popular myth that elephants go to a special place to die. However, they do go off alone to die. They also take an interest in elephant bones. One young elephant, on finding the jawbone of its dead mother, spent a day fondling it. Elephants have been seen covering their dead with leaves and branches.

Elephants often entwine trunks and clash their ivory tusks together in play.

Elephants

ALTHOUGH THESE magnificent animals are still wild, elephants have been used by humans as beasts of burden for thousands of years. Hannibal, a famous general, took 38 elephants with his army across the Alps in 218 BC. Even today, elephants are decorated and ridden in festivals and used to carry heavy loads across land.

AT ONE TIME, elephants lived in most parts of the world but as humans cultivated the land, the areas in which elephants could roam became fewer and fewer.

Today, the only elephants are found in India and Africa and even they are threatened with extinction. They are hunted for their ivory tusks, so most of them that survive live in protected parks and reserves.

Elephants spend between 18 and 20 hours a day eating up to 250 kg (550 lb) of vegetation. They use their long trunks to suck up around 100 litres (1.2 gallons) of water.

People who work closely with animals believe that elephants have strong emotional ties to one another. They are highly intelligent and sensitive creatures and contact with family and other elephants is extremely important to them. Elephant babies like to touch their mum whilst they feed.

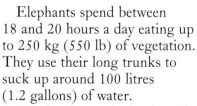

Hindu temples in India keep stables of elephants. The animals are decorated and ridden in ceremonial processions.

ELEPHANTS SOMETIMES PLAY FOOTBALL WITH BALLS OF EARTH.

situations that would make us sad, such as being captured, injured, scolded, separated from their families or when a close friend dies. One photograph shows a young circus elephant with tears rolling down its cheeks as it stands with chains cutting deep into its ankles.

Elephants can show compassion, supporting sick or injured members of their group by propping them up on either side and slowing down the group's pace so that they all stay together. One female elephant in Murchison Falls National Park, USA, carried her dead calf around for three days, scraped a shallow grave under a tree, buried the calf and stood guard for a few more days, eating nothing until finally she left the site.

ELEPHANTS PURR IF THEY LOSE SIGHT OF EACH OTHER IN THE WILD.

Ganesha

Ganesha is the Hindu god of wisdom and good luck, the 'Remover of Obstacles' whose power is called upon at the start of a journey or important task. An elephant-headed god who rides on the back of a rat, he is sometimes shown sitting on a lotus surrounded by a ring of skulls. Statues of this god are found mainly in India, but also in other parts of Asia.

Indian or African?

The most obvious difference between African and Indian elephants is size. The African elephant is about 3.4 m (11 ft) tall at the shoulder and has much larger ears than the Indian elephant. The Indian elephant grows to 3 m (10 ft) at its tallest point – the arch of its slightly humped back.

ELEPHANTS ARE THE LARGEST LIVING LAND MAMMALS ON EARTH.

One young elephant, living in an elephant orphanage in Kenya, would drink only from a bottle if it could stick its trunk into the ear of its human foster mother!

Elephants sometimes look as if they are crying as their eyes water heavily at times, often in

ELEPHANT ARTISTS

Tildy, an elephant in New York Zoo, USA, was seen scratching drawings in the dust with a stick. Its keeper gave it pots of paints and a long brush and before long it had created enough paintings for an exhibition. In 1980, the keeper of Siri, a young Indian elephant, gave it a pencil and a drawing pad and it began to draw with enthusiasm. Samples of the work were sent to artists and one comment was that they showed 'flair, decisiveness and originality'. Many captive elephants use sticks or stones to draw. In fact, Carol, an Indian elephant in San Diego Zoo, USA, paints with colours, as does Ruby, an Asian elephant who lives in Phoenix, Arizona, USA.

WWF

The giant panda is used as the logo for WWF (World Wide Fund for Nature). WWF chose the panda as it is the best loved of all the endangered species. WWF began work on panda conservation in China in 1980 and has spent over £7 million there. WWF has worked with the Chinese government to establish 14 new reserves, covering a total of 7,800 km sq (3,000 sq mi) of their 18,100 km sq (7,000 sq mi) habitat that will be protected forever.

Panda's Stare

Many animals are instinctively afraid of two large eyes staring directly at them, as in the wild it can be taken as a sign of attack. The panda's huge black circles around its eyes exaggerate this stare especially as, at a distance, its ears can look like two more eyes, doubling its threatening power!

Giant pandas

ALTHOUGH THEY HAVE been living on Earth for millions of years and were once the pets of Chinese emperors, giant pandas are now extremely rare, endangered animals that live in six small mountainous forest areas of China. Solitary animals that spend most of their time alone in the wild, they are exceedingly shy of humans. They are, however, one of the most popular and best-loved animals.

THE GIANT PANDA STANDS between 1.2-1.5 m (4-5 ft) tall, has a 12.5 cm (5 in) tail and weighs an average of 80-100 kg (176-221 lb). The giant panda is very furry – even the soles of its feet are covered in hair. The black and white fur is not soft and silky as it looks from a distance but hard, coarse and thick.

Pandas are carnivores that have adapted to their environment and have mainly a vegetarian diet.

They eat fish and rodents but 99 percent of what they eat is made up of the stem, shoots and leaves of the bamboo plant. Pandas have an elongated wrist bone that acts rather like our thumb, allowing them to hold the bamboo stalks while they chew them.

UNLIKE OTHER BEARS, GIANT PANDAS DO NOT HIBERNATE.

Large areas of bamboo forests are being cleared regularly, making life harder and harder for the giant panda.

TINY PANDA BABIES WEIGH AS LITTLE AS 100 G (3 OZ) AT BIRTH.

Hidden in the forest, the panda spends most of its time eating. In fact, it gets through about 1.5 kg (33 lb) of bamboo in only 14 hours – that's about 10 percent of its body weight. A panda only digests a small amount of its food and bamboo is very poor in nutrients, so this is probably why it eats such a lot and so fast.

JOYFUL PANDA

Pandas rarely show their emotions in an obvious way. They are one of the most difficult animals to understand, their faces showing little of their feelings or reactions. However, one two-year-old panda from a Chinese centre had spent most of its life in a darkened cage. One day it was moved to an outdoor enclosure. Immediately, the panda erupted into a ball of joy. It pranced up a hill in the compound and then somersaulted all the way down. It repeated this over and over again, unable to contain its pleasure at being outside and free to play in the wild.

Although the bamboo plant can take between 10 and 100 years to flower, once it has produced seeds it dies. The seeds may take several years to grow into new plants. During this time, the pandas have to either change their diet or travel to where the bamboo has not yet flowered just to survive.

IN 1869, PERE ARMAND DAVID WAS THE FIRST EUROPEAN TO DESCRIBE THE GIANT PANDA.

Giant pandas are under threat because of the destruction of the bamboo forests, which leaves fewer and fewer places for them to live and eat. Today, there are fewer than 1,000 wild pandas alive on Earth.

Magical Pandas

Until AD 2, the panda was considered rare and semi-divine in China. From 206 BC to AD 24, Chinese emperors kept rare beasts in the palace gardens and the most treasured of these were the pandas. The Chinese poet Bai Juyo wrote that the panda had magical powers that could ward off evil spirits and natural disasters, and prevent disease.

Black Eyes

Legends tell that a long time ago, when the panda's fur was pure white, one of its friends was a young girl. They often laughed and played together happily. One day, a hungry tiger crept up on them. The tiger was about to kill the panda when the panda's friend rushed to stop the attack and was instead killed herself. The panda was so distressed that it rubbed black ashes on its arms as a sign of mourning and cried for a long time, rubbing its eyes with its paws. From that day onward, the panda has had black rings around its eyes.

Unicorns

The unicorn is a mythical creature from medieval legend. It looks just like a horse but has a long single horn growing from its head. The unicorn's horn was said to have purified a poisoned pool, allowing fellow animals to drink from the pool before dusk.

Famous Horse

Clever Hans was a famous counting horse. In front of a crowd, his trainer would ask him to perform multiplication sums such as two times four. Hans would tap out the answer with his foot – in this case, eight. How did he do it? Hans used his naturally heightened senses to pick up on the tiny eyebrow movements of his trainer, which he made just before Hans was nearing the correct number of taps!

The horses of the Camargue, in France, live in the wild, but are used to herd cattle.

Horses

PERHAPS MORE THAN most animals, horses have been drawn into the world of humans. For centuries they have been used in hunting, farming, as pack horses, harnessed to pull carts, carriages, ploughs and chariots, taken into wars and used for entertainment. Humans and horses have forged many friendships, from small children and their ponies to Alexander the Great and his beloved horse Bucephalus.

LONG AGO, WILD HORSES were stalked by carnivorous predators such as big cats and wolves. Since these enemies were some of the fastest and stealthiest animals on the planet, horses needed excellent instincts to survive and they developed one

THERE ARE OVER 100 BREEDS OF DOMESTICATED HORSE.

of the most sensitive alarm systems in nature. Despite centuries of association with humans, horses still retain strong survival instincts.

Even in darkness, they can see movements unnoticed by most other species, including humans.

For centuries horses have been working for people's benefit.

SOME RACE HORSES GALLOP AT MORE THAN 64 KM/H (40 MPH).

Frank Bell, an American horse-whisperer who studied the ways of the American Plains Indians with horses, says that when he makes contact with a new horse the most important thing is the first impression he makes on the horse, as it is the first impression that links directly to these age-old instincts. The horse looks to see if he should run away or if it is

They can hear tiny sounds beyond human hearing and can smell a carnivore at great distance. Because they are naturally fearful, any unknown or unexpected thing picked up by these senses causes a horse to react in alarm and try to follow its basic instinct to run away for survival.

WHEN HORSES WALK, THEY MOVE THEIR DIAGONALLY OPPOSITE LEGS AT THE SAME TIME.

If a horse is treated roughly or mishandled, its basic nature can take over and that first instinct to run from danger will be very strong. It will try to get away and so, often, will become labelled as wild or unmanageable.

ADULT HORSES HAVE BETWEEN 40 AND 42 TEETH.

Horse-whisperers are trainers who work to understand these deep instincts of fear and self-protection by flight. They use gentle, calm gestures to allay a horse's fear and build up trust.

LIFE LINE

Once a horse and a bull shared the same field on a farm. The bull was sold and the horse soon became ill. A vet was called but he couldn't find anything medically wrong with the horse. The only conclusion he could draw was that the horse was dying of a broken heart. The farmer called the new owner of the bull and asked him to lead the bull to his telephone receiver. The farmer then held her receiver to the horse's mouth and made it whinny. On hearing the noise, the bull pricked up its ears and bellowed loudly. The horse whinnied back, and so began the world's oddest telephone conversation! This became a daily ritual until the horse made a full recovery.

safe to stay. Using caresses and strokes to soothe the horse, Bell gradually transforms the horse's instinctive distrust of humans. The horse is then willing to do anything for him because it trusts him. Bell says, "The word 'love' is not inappropriate."

Horseshoes

Most horses are fitted with metal shoes to protect their hooves on hard roads and surfaces. The first horseshoes were made of leather and called 'hipposandals'. Horseshoes are believed to be lucky but only if they are hung with the opening at the top!

Comanche

Captain Keogh of the US cavalry rode a horse, called Comanche, in the Battle of the Little Big Horn in 1876. Although wounded and hardly able to stand, Comanche carried his master for many hours. Comanche's heroic deed has made him one of the most famous horses in America.

At the end of the battle, Comanche was the only horse left alive.

Buffalo Dance

In southern France, cave paintings dating from around 10,000-30,000 BC, show masked men luring buffalo towards a cliff to be killed on the rocks below by acting out a lively dance step. The Blackfoot Indians of Alberta, Canada, and Montana, USA, used to hunt buffalo in a similar way. Legend has it that the Blackfoot Indians learned the slow and solemn ritual dance from the buffalo after a young woman agreed to marry a bull buffalo, in exchange for the herd sacrificing themselves so her tribe could eat.

Buffalo and bison

THESE MAJESTIC CREATURES are powerful and strong – the males, called bulls, can weigh over a ton! Despite their huge size, they are surprisingly agile and can reach top speeds of 48 km/h (30 mph). Native Americans relied heavily on the buffalo. Its meat provided food, its hide was used to make clothes and shelter and its bones became tools and knives.

IN EUROPE AND ASIA, the buffalo is called a 'bison'. It is an impressive animal, with a great shaggy head and powerful, humped shoulders, both covered in a cape of brown-black fur. Male buffalo usually weigh in at about 725 kg (1,600 lb).

ONE WHITE BUFFALO IS BORN FOR EVERY FIVE MILLION BROWN BUFFALO.

Female buffalo, called cows, weigh quite a bit less at 453 kg (1,000 lb).

BUFFALOS ENJOY LYING IN WATER AND WALLOWING IN MUD.

They stand around 1.9 m (6.2 ft) tall at the shoulders, with a 2-3.5 m (6-11 ft) body length – that's larger than the African buffalo, which has a body length of around 2 m (6-9 ft).

The African buffalo has larger, curved horns and a much smaller mane. It is the most aggressive of all the buffalo, capable of defeating a lion. The longest horns grown by any animal are those of the Indian buffalo. On the curve, they can measure over 4 m (13 ft) from tip to tip.

Buffalo are primarily grazers, herbivores that feed in both the morning and the evening. They rest during the day, chewing the cud or wallowing in water, mud or dust to rid themselves of the parasites that live on their bodies.

Once the buffalo herds on the American plains looked like brown seas, stretching from horizon to horizon. Thomas Farnham, while travelling the Santa Fe Trail, Mexico, in 1839, was in the midst of a buffalo herd for three days. He estimated there were well over a million of them covering an area about 3,497 km sq (1,350 sq mi).

ONE HERD OF BUFFALO IN ZIMBABWE HAS BEEN LED BY AN ELEPHANT FOR 20 YEARS.

The vast herds were made up of smaller family groups of 50-100 and were usually led by an old female.

Buffalo Birds

Two birds stay close to a buffalo throughout the whole of its life. The cattle egret perches on its back, flying down to grab the insects disturbed by the buffalo's hooves in the grass. The oxpecker stays even closer, feeding on the ticks in the buffalo's hide. It lives almost permanently on the buffalo's back, sometimes even courting and mating there.

AWKWARD BUFFALO

Herdsman Michel Pablo made three attempts to round up some buffalo he had sold to the Canadian government. First he tried to load them into a cattle truck and led by an old bull, the group trotted into the railway yard. Without changing pace the group trotted up the ramp into the truck, smashed through the wooden rear and carried on trotting back up the valley and away. Next they were herded into a pen against a steep cliff wall. The group ran straight into the pen and out again – up the cliff! Finally, when a small group were successfully captured, a big bull splintered the planking with its horns and led the group to freedom.

Buffalo and bison were hunted almost to extinction. Today the bison herds in the USA have grown to about 35,000.

Howling Wolves

Wolves have a complex communication system that uses scent markings, body language (which includes movement of hair, ears and tail), facial gestures, eye contact and vocal sounds, from whimpers through to whines, barks and the famous howls. Howls can be just for fun, a greeting, to locate other pack members, a danger signal or a warning to a trespasser on pack territory.

Wolf and Crane

A small meat bone was stuck in the wolf's throat. The crane agreed to try and remove it. It stuck its long neck down the wolf's throat and pulled out the bone. When the crane asked for a reward the wolf replied, 'Be content. You have put your head inside a wolf's mouth and taken it out again in safety. That ought to be reward enough for you!'

Wolves survive freezing temperatures by lying with their backs to the wind, tucking their noses between their legs and covering their faces with their thick tails.

Wolves

WOLVES ARE TRULY wild creatures, yet they live in social structures with very defined rules. Within their packs, which rarely have more than 12 members, disobedience and unruly behaviour are not tolerated. Each pack is led by a dominant pair, the alpha male and alpha female, who stay together for life. The alpha male signals its rank by carrying its tail higher than the others.

THE WHOLE PACK shows great loyalty to the alpha pair, who are treated with great affection and tolerance. Wolves show respect by folding back their tails between their legs.

If the alpha female gives birth, the pack is responsible for rearing her pups. Before the pups are born, the mother digs

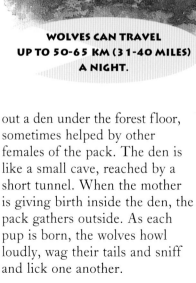

WOLVES CAN TRAVEL UP TO 50-65 KM (31-40 MILES) A NIGHT.

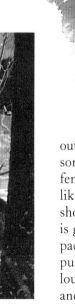

out a den under the forest floor, sometimes helped by other females of the pack. The den is like a small cave, reached by a short tunnel. When the mother is giving birth inside the den, the pack gathers outside. As each pup is born, the wolves howl loudly, wag their tails and sniff and lick one another.

Wolves howl to keep in touch with each other or to warn other packs to stay away.

the challenger shows submission, often by lying on its back with its throat exposed.

A wolf has extremely sharp hearing and a sense of smell that is more than a thousand times more acute than a human's. Its pointed nose encourages air to circulate around the odour-sensitive cells inside. One researcher found a five-month-old cub that had picked up the smell of a porcupine in a field 1.5 km (1 mile) away.

Pack members hunt together, co-operating to run down prey such as deer, caribou and wild horses. They also eat small animals such as mice, fish and crabs.

A WOLF CAN EAT UP TO 9 KG (20 LB) OF FOOD AT ANY ONE TIME.

The two main species of wolf are the grey wolf and the smaller red wolf. The grey wolf varies in size and coat colour, from all black to the white of the Arctic wolf. An adult male great wolf averages 40 kg (88 lb) in weight and 1.5-2 m (5-6.5 ft) in length.

Wolf pups are carefully raised and trained. While the pack goes out to hunt, one wolf, called the aunt, stays behind with the pups.

Squabbles in a wolf pack are frequent but controlled. The dominant animal soon prevails and

THE MANED WOLF AND THE CRAB-EATING WOLF ARE MAINLY NOCTURNAL.

Romulus and Remus

In 8 BC, Romulus and Remus were baby twin heirs to the throne of Latium. Their uncle ordered the babies to be killed but a servant put them in a wooden chest on the River Tiber instead. This was washed on to the banks near the site of present-day Rome. There, a she-wolf found the twins and brought them up until they were adopted by Faustulus, one of the royal shepherds.

Happy Eater

It is said that when the wolf eats, all eat. In winter, when wolves have eaten their fill of a kill, small mammals such as hares, weasels, porcupines, mice and voles come to nibble on the flesh, while birds swoop down to grab a beak-full.

LONG MEMORY

A naturalist exploring the Canadian wilderness came upon a she-wolf caught by her foot in a trap. Her pup sat beside her. The pair had obviously been there for some time and were both very hungry. The naturalist fed the pup and slept nearby until he felt the wolf trusted him. He then released her. The wolf then made it clear she wanted him to follow and led him to her pack. The naturalist stayed with the pack for a few days, until the pack moved on. Some years later, the naturalist was camping in the same area, when a wolf appeared and stood gazing at him. By its scarred foot he recognised it as the same wolf he had saved.

Fox, Ass and Lion

The fox, ass and lion went hunting together. After catching their prey, the ass divided the spoils into three piles. The lion roared with anger because it wanted all the food and killed the ass. The fox, wanting to stay alive, put the meat in one pile and offered it to the lion saying it was happy with the scraps. To this day the fox still eats scraps.

Many red foxes live in towns and cities. They scavenge from dustbins and rubbish tips after dark.

Foxes

THE FOLKLORE OF MANY countries sees the fox as a trickster – a magical animal able to change shape, and always having the intent to deceive. This is probably because foxes can quickly adapt their behaviour to different circumstances and can creep around unseen. Foxes are well-known for their cunning and slyness but are also admired for their alertness, intelligence and keen skills of observation.

THE RED FOX IS the most common of all the foxes. It is found in the USA, Canada, Europe, Australia and much of Asia and in nearly all habitats from mountain tops and sand dunes to salt marshes and town centres. Each red fox family holds its own territory, which may be as small as 200 m squared (77 sq ft) for foxes that have adapted to town life, and as large as 65 km squared (25 square mi) for foxes in hill country. Foxes are cautious by nature and only come out of hiding at dusk. Most town sightings of foxes happen as they are caught in car headlights while crossing the road.

A fox's senses are keen. It is able to see movement and objects on the very edge of its field of vision. It is a master of stealth and camouflage and makes

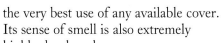

the very best use of any available cover. Its sense of smell is also extremely highly developed.

Foxes have a wide and varied diet, eating mainly small mammals, earthworms, beetles, fruit and carrion. Urban foxes steal food from dustbins, bird tables, compost heaps and rubbish dumps. They are scavengers rather than predators.

BAT-EARED FOXES HAVE LARGE EARS. THEY HUNT THEIR PREY BY SOUND.

Arctic foxes could not survive without previously buried food stores to rely on. They tend to kill everything in sight, probably responding to a need to obtain extra food for storage, even though they cannot carry away all they have destroyed. Arctic foxes have excellent memories, burying surplus food in many places and remembering each one. The icy climate keeps their supply of dead birds, animals and even eggs prey well-preserved.

A FOX'S TAIL IS CALLED A BRUSH.

When it comes to eating, male foxes, called dogs, usually eat more than females, called vixens. However, when their cubs are born, the dog goes to great trouble to bring food for the vixen, even going without himself until she is full. The dog continues with this behaviour until the cubs are able to fend for themselves in the wild. Then, he returns to a more independent way of life, looking after only himself.

Play is important to a fox and both the dog-fox and the vixen play with their cubs. They have

at least 22 play signals and also seem to communicate inaudibly. One vixen was spotted watching from the den entrance as her three cubs played nearby. One of the cubs set off determinedly across the field to the far hedge. Immediately the vixen rose to her feet, stood very still and pointed her muzzle in its direction.

Young male cubs leave the den, but young females stay, which sometimes leaves up to five vixens with one dominant dog fox.

CUNNING CREATURES

When in danger, foxes use every trick in the book to survive. One fox was seen being chased by hounds. It came to a stream, across which an old tree had fallen, ran halfway across the log, peered over the side and spotted a tiny island of dry ground in the middle of the stream. It jumped down to this tiny island, then leapt back on to the bank it had just come from and ran off. Not long after, the hounds came to the log, sniffed the fox's scent and ran across it to the other bank where suddenly they lost the scent. After running round in circles for some time, the hounds finally gave up the chase.

In a few seconds, the cub slowed, turned, looked at its mother and hurried back home.

Foxes have been, and still are, treated cruelly by humankind. They are often hunted as a sport and killed by fur trappers. Worldwide, foxes are one of the most persecuted mammals.

Inari

Inari is the Japanese god of food, or goddess of rice, and is both male and female. His/her messenger is the fox and it is believed that he/she can change into a fox. In many Japanese households Inari is seen as a symbol of prosperity and friendship, and many Japanese towns have Inari shrines guarded by statues of foxes. Inari's central temple Fushimi-Inara, in south-east Kyoto city, was built around AD 700.

Snake Charming

A popular belief is that snakes can be charmed into a trance by flute music. In fact, this is completely untrue. Snakes have no ear membranes and are deaf to all but the lowest frequencies. It is not the sound of the snake charmer's flute that affects the snake but the swaying movements of the man and pipe and the vibrations of sound travelling through the ground!

Did You Know...

A Jacobson's organ is a small pouch found in the mouths of snakes and other reptiles. It is lined with special cells, which allow the snake to sense and track its prey by tasting the air, water or ground when it flicks its tongue in and out. A snake flicks its forked tongue out every few seconds.

Serpent Staff

Adopted as the badge of the British Royal Army Medical Corps, this symbol of a staff with two snakes twisted around it was the emblem of Asclepius, the Greek god of medicine. The magic wand of Hermes, the Greek messenger of the gods, had silver wings and two snakes coiled round it. The Bible tells of Moses lifting up a brass snake with the power to heal all those that looked on it.

Snakes

FOR CENTURIES, people around the world have been both fascinated and frightened by snakes. In eastern countries snakes are symbols of new beginnings and transformations, probably because they regularly shed their skins and emerge with new ones. In the Christian religion, snakes have often been seen as evil, their form taken by the devil to tempt Eve in the Garden of Eden.

THE MOST OBVIOUS thing about snakes is that they have no limbs. With no arms or legs, it seems as if they glide along by magic. In fact, snakes move by hitching their scales over rough parts of the ground and then extending the body forward from those anchor points.

RATTLESNAKES SHAKE THEIR TAILS TO MAKE A LOUD WHIRRING NOISE.

Although some snakes give the impression of fast movement, it is in fact an illusion. Except for short bursts, most snakes cannot keep up with a person walking at normal brisk pace – 6.5 km/h (4mph) – and a human hand can snatch an object faster than most snakes can strike.

The fastest-moving land snake in the world is the slender black mamba, which is found south of the Sahara desert, Africa. It has been timed moving at a

Snakes have no eyelids. Their eyes are protected by clear scales.

speed of 11 km/h (7 mph) over short distances.

A snake sheds its skin regularly as it grows by rubbing its body against a rough surface, such as a tree trunk or a rock. Underneath, a new skin is revealed with bright, clean scales.

SNAKES SHED THEIR SKIN IN ONE PIECE, TURNING IT INSIDE OUT AS THEY WRIGGLE OUT.

Some snakes are poisonous. They have fangs and venom glands. They mostly use their venom to kill prey, although they have been known to use poison in self-defence, biting an attacker and then injecting venom into the wound. Some vipers are among the most dangerous snakes. The 163 species of viper have large fangs that fold away when not in use. Less than a quarter of all snakes are venomous.

As well as poisonous snakes, constrictors are dangerous too. These giant snakes kill their prey by gripping with their jaws, then wrapping their bodies in tight coils around the victim, stopping them from breathing.

A BABY COBRA IS DEADLY FROM THE TIME IT HATCHES.

In 1996, a giant python was caught near Tenang, Malaysia, coiled around the body of a rubber worker whose head was in its mouth. It had already squeezed him to death. The python was 6.6 m (21 ft) long, 76 cm (2.5 ft) in diameter and weighed 140 kg (309 lb).

Snakes live in many different places: in the sea, underground in burrows, in the desert, and even up trees.

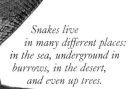

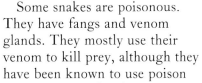

Nagas

In Hindi myth, Nagas are a race of serpent demons whose power comes from a jewel embedded in their throats or skulls. Their name means 'those who do not walk, but creep'. When the gods passed around the cup containing the elixir of immortality, the Nagas grabbed it but spilled some drops on the ground. As they licked up the drops, the grass split their tongues, which have remained forked ever since.

Unblinking Stare

Snakes have no eyelids. Legend tells that a long time ago, in Australia, Biame, the Good Spirit lived there with all the creatures. Most of the time they lived happily, except when Ngar-ang, the Storm Spirit, came by on the back of his Thunderbird. One day, Biame told all the creatures not to look up or open their eyes as Ngar-ang rushed past in the darkness. All the creatures obeyed except the snake, who couldn't resist one quick look. When Ngar-ang saw two bright little eyes shining at him, he swooped down to fight Biame. As a punishment Biame took away the snake's eyelids.

THE 'COBRA-GRANDE'

The Amazon river, in South America, is the largest body of fresh water on Earth. It is also supposedly home to the 'cobra-grande', a huge river snake that can swallow deer whole. Since 1906, regular sightings of this monster have been reported, and wide furrowed tracks have been seen in swamps leading from the river to lakes. At one stage, a team from the National Institute of Amazonian Research went to investigate one sighting, getting there just in time to stop the Brazilian army from bombing a lake to kill the snake. Despite this, no one has ever seen more than a glimpse of a huge, horned head or something that creates huge ripples on the surface of the water.

Black Cats

In the past, cats were believed to have mystical powers or to be connected with witches and it is partly because of this that some people still consider cats to be a sign of good luck. If you meet a black cat and stroke it three times or if one runs across your path, it brings good fortune. If a black cat comes uninvited into your house you should never chase it away. However, if a black cat walks across the stage during a theatre performance, it is said to bring disaster.

The Egyptians worshipped the cat goddess Bastet. Her annual festival was a national celebration.

Cats

DOMESTIC CATS CAN have special relationships with people. It is sometimes said that cats are the only tame animals that can look a person in the eye without flinching. Despite having a close relationship with humans for over 4,000 years, cats are fiercely independent and must be won over. Only then will they allow their keepers to care for and love them.

THERE IS AN old English proverb that reads, 'In the eyes of a cat all things belong to cats'. Cats come and go as they please, when they please, and if neglected may move on to someone more worthy of their affections. However, when love is truly given by a cat, it can be extremely affectionate and loyal.

THE ROMANS SAW THE CAT AS A SYMBOL OF LIBERTY.

Cats are loners, solitary hunters who roam the dark, mysterious world of twilight and pre-dawn. Even a cat that likes to sit on a windowsill and stare out at the world for days on end will suddenly respond to the call of the wild and venture out, maybe to mark its territory in relation to that of neighbouring cats.

A CAT STANDS ITS FUR ON END TO MAKE ITSELF LOOK BIGGER.

A cat living in the wild needs a territory in which to catch food, so the bigger this area the better.

Although domestic cats do not have this keen sense of survival, the instinct to claim territory still remains, especially for male cats, called toms. Toms may establish a territory 10 times larger than that of female cats, called queens. Two cats in one house will also establish their own territories within the house.

Like their huge relations, lions, cats use their energy in short bursts and spend a great deal of time sleeping – curled up if cold, or stretched out if warm and relaxed.

WHEN A CAT IS FRIGHTENED, ITS PAWS SWEAT.

Unlike the lion, who eats about once a week, cats like to eat a few small meals throughout the day. Any change of routine can cause them to lose their appetite for a while.

Cats communicate with their whole bodies.

Cats make good pets. They are clean, independent and love to sit on your lap!

Cat's Eyes

During the day a cat's pupils are narrow slits but after dark they open wide to let in as much light as possible. A cat's night vision is six times more sensitive than a human's. Cat's eyes glow in the dark because of a special layer of cells at the back of the eyes, which reflect light just like a mirror.

MAN'S BEST FRIEND?

A man in the German town of Magdenburg used to stroke and talk to a stray cat he passed every day on his way to work. One morning in 1944, during World War II, he was shaving when he heard a cat mewing at the door. On the step was the stray cat. The cat was agitated and rubbed up against the man and seemed to want him to leave the house. The man left and the cat led him about 1 km (0.6 miles) away, looking back all the while to check he was still following. Suddenly, overhead, came the roar of the British Royal Air Force Lancaster bombers and then the terrible sound of bombs. The man's house was flattened but the stray cat had saved his life.

Cats enjoy prowling in gardens and fields.

For example, a cat pricks its ears forward when alert or out hunting, twitches them when nervous or lays them flat against its head if very frightened or aggressive. If a cat gently flicks its tail it is showing pleasure if relaxed, or readiness to pounce if hunting. If it starts to thrash its tail around, it is indicating anger.

Manx Cats

Manx cats have no tails and it is said they are native to the Isle of Man. Legend has it that invaders of the island cut off the tails to decorate their helmets. Mother cats, to save their kittens from harm, bit off their tails at birth, until eventually, the kittens were born tailless. However, it is more likely that Manx cats were imported from Phoenician traders or entered aboard ships from the Spanish Armada in the 16th century.

Argus

The ancient Greek hero, Odysseus, went to war while his dog, Argus, was still a puppy. The dog grew and served others until he was old, neglected and cast out to sleep on a dunghill. When Odysseus eventually came home, this is where he found his beloved dog. Argus, too old to move, wagged his tail with joy and died. He had waited 20 years and saw his master again at last.

St. Bernards are a large breed of dog, famous for their use as rescue dogs in mountainous areas.

Dogs

ABOVE ALL OTHER domesticated animals, dogs show humankind unconditional love and loyalty. They have been man's faithful companions throughout recorded history. Dogs have worked for human causes too – from guiding the blind to helping the police force. A dog can truly be called 'man's best friend'.

DOGS ARE THE DESCENDANTS of wolves and coyotes – they are wild dogs that have been domesticated, and are most like their wild cousins when they howl. Careful breeding over thousands of years has created the several hundred breeds of dog that exist today.

Throughout the ages dogs have been bred or trained to do different things: herd sheep and cattle, hunt, kill or retrieve game and work as police dogs or guide dogs. Others are used as guard dogs, or bred for use in sports such as greyhound racing. Some dogs are chosen for their natural hardiness to pull sledges through ice and snow, or act as 'living blankets' for shepherds on cold nights out on the mountains.

A DOG STICKS OUT ITS TONGUE AND PANTS TO COOL DOWN.

A DOG WALKS ON TIPTOES – ON THE END OF ITS FEET.

In many ways, the dog has been of service to humankind over the years and as a result each variety of breed has qualities that are unique.

Dogs love exercise and need to be walked at least once a day.

Some love water, some need to run miles and miles each day, some prefer cold weather, others a warm climate.

A dog's strongest sense is smell. And one of the things it loves to do is roll. Sometimes if it rolls in something that to us smells foul, it seems as if to the dog it is even more pleasurable. If a dog comes home covered in muck it has probably had the dog equivalent of a day at the funfair!

DOGS WERE FIRST DOMESTICATED IN THE STONE AGE.

Many people believe dogs have second sight and can predict death. This may be because the human body goes through chemical changes when near to death and dogs can smell these chemical changes.

If anyone thinks animals do not have emotions, they only have to watch a dog showing unrestrained

CHIHUAHUAS ARE NAMED AFTER THE STATE OF CHIHUAHUA IN MEXICO.

DOGS CAN IDENTIFY ONE MOLECULE OF SCENT IN A MILLION.

joy and delight when its owners return after a trip away, when a walk is suggested or if it is let off the lead to run free. A dog does not pretend. Leaping, running and barking are all real expressions of the joy it is feeling at that moment.

A dog also feels shame when it has done something wrong. Often a dog knows its human family will be angry at it and greets them crouched low and with its head down as a sign of submission.

A dog's great loyalty, even when cruelly treated, is amazing. It takes a lot to break its spirit.

ALSATION SAVIOUR

During World War II, a watchman at the naval airbase of De Koog, The Netherlands, had his attention attracted one day by an Alsation. The large dog came to the gate, whined and scraped his paw on the ground and then ran off. The dog repeated this action every 10 minutes or so. Eventually the watchman followed the dog and was led to a seriously injured dog nearby, which had obviously been run over by a car. Once the Alsation knew help had come, it began to lick the other dog's wounds and stood over the dog when it started to rain. The Dutch Society for the Protection of Animals took both dogs in as they seemed to be strays.

A dog's greatest gift is its loyalty and faithfulness, often to the point of self-sacrifice. Jane was a dog who was devoted to her owner, Brian. One day, Brian went climbing, leaving Jane by his jacket and telling her to 'stay'. While climbing, Brian fell and was taken to hospital. When he woke he had amnesia and couldn't recall anything. Fifteen days later, his memory returned and he remembered Jane. When he found her she was still there, almost dead, standing on guard where he had left her.

Beddgelert

Beddgelert, a small village in Wales, UK, derived its name from an old legend. The story tells of Prince Llywelyn who left his faithful hound, Gelert, looking after his son while he went out hunting. On his return to the lodge, he was met by Gelert, his mouth and paws dripping with blood. Horrified, the prince saw his baby's crib was overturned and the child missing. The prince drove his sword into Gelert and killed him. Then, hearing a faint cry, he found the baby safe but beside it the dead body of a wolf, killed by Gelert to save the child. Deeply distressed, the prince buried Gelert and placed a craved stone over the grave so that all would know of his bravery.

Feeding Habits

A dog will usually eat until full. There are, however, stories of dogs that rise above this basic instinct. One story tells of a female hound dog which fell into a rock crevasse in Tennessee, USA, without its owners knowing. A male dog, which lived in the same house, ate only a small amount of his food each day, then gathered up the rest and ran off. When rescuers found the bitch ten days later, it was obvious the male dog had been dropping his food into the crevasse to feed her.

Ape Men

A Philippine myth tells of Bathala, the only living being in the world, who took a lump of clay to make humankind. He had almost finished shaping the clay when it slipped from his hand. As he grabbed for it, part of the clay stretched into a tail. Bathala said, "you will become an ape and live in the trees!" He then made humans.

Life for mountain gorillas is relatively peaceful, although leaders occasionally have to drive intruders away from their females.

Apes

WE LIKE TO THINK we are very different from other animals but when it comes to the great apes, it is obvious we are very closely related. In fact, chimpanzees are almost 99 percent genetically identical to us. Like us, apes form strong family groups, are intelligent, have feelings and emotions and use tools.

THE APES (gorillas, chimpanzees, gibbons and orang-utans) are all primates. Gorillas are the largest primates and because of their size and great strength they have often been labelled as stupid and dangerously fierce.

This is not true. They are slow, gentle and intelligent creatures that form close relationships. Mountain gorillas live in groups that usually include a single adult male, one or two immature males, two to four adult females and two to five young gorillas under eight years old. They travel slowly

AN ADULT MALE GORILLA CAN WEIGH AS MUCH AS 270 KG (595 LB).

KOKO KNOWS OVER 1,000 SIGNED WORDS AND UNDERSTANDS OVER 2,000 SPOKEN WORDS.

through the forest, eating food before moving on to another feeding ground.

Chimpanzees live in groups of varying sizes – sometimes just males, females with young or mixed groups. They often fight with neighbouring chimpanzee groups. A group's home area depends on its size, but usually it lives deep in the forests or on open grassland. Of all the apes, chimpanzees remind us most of ourselves because of the facial expressions they make and the way they play games, solve puzzles and make and use tools.

Apes cannot make the sounds of human speech but they are capable of understanding spoken languages and some have learned to use sign language, such as Koko, the gorilla, who has been using it for 25 years.

CHIMPANZEES ARE THE MOST INTELLIGENT OF ALL ANIMALS.

Both Koko and a chimpanzee called Lana have invented their own sign words for things. For example, Lana calls a duck a 'water-bird' and Koko calls a ring a 'finger-bracelet'.

Mountain gorillas spend their time eating plant food and ranging their home territory, which can be 10-39 km sq (4-15 sq mi).

Orang-utans spend most of their time high up in trees searching for fruit, shoots or insects.

In April 1998, Koko took part in a live conversation via the Internet (a typist keyed in Koko's signed conversation). The entire 45-minute 'chat' was videotaped.

Through the use of this sign language, apes are changing the way we see them. We have assumed that because animals cannot express their feelings in language, they do not have those feelings. Now we know that for some species, at least, that may not be the case.

Declaration on Apes

The '*Declaration on Great Apes*' was first published in 1993. It sets out a declaration of rights for apes. The declaration states, among other things, that apes should not be killed, except in very strict circumstances, such as self-defence, that humans should protect apes' liberty and not imprison them unnecessarily and that apes should not be tortured by deliberate infliction of severe pain. It is hoped the declaration will play an important role in producing required social change.

Clever Chimps

Some years ago, scientists at the University of Pennsylvania, Philadelphia, USA, demonstrated that chimpanzees had a concept of numbers, including fractions, and could match up completely different types of objects in which the only factor in common was a mathematical similarity. Today, at the Ohio State University, USA, researchers are discovering exactly the same ability in their chimpanzees.

CHILD RESCUE

On 16 August 1996, a three-year-old boy fell 5.5 m (18 ft) into the gorilla enclosure at Brookfield Zoo in Jersey, US. All six gorillas rushed to help but first on the scene was Binti Jua (Swahili for 'Daughter of Sunshine') with her 17-month-old baby clinging to her back. She gently picked up the boy, cradled him in her lap, then carried him across the compound to the human access door and laid him down so the keepers could rescue him. Binti is the niece of the famous gorilla Koko. Binti was taken from her own mother at birth and sent to San Francisco Zoo, USA, when she was just three months old.

Celebrations

As humans, we all celebrate certain rituals that traditionally follow the calendar year. We hold many different festivals throughout the year for example, New Year, birthdays and anniversaries of certain events. We know from the Bible that birthdays were first celebrated at least 4,000 years ago.

Human Evolution

Early in the 20th century, when scientists were deciding how the human species evolved, they looked at the shape of the human skull and compared it with the fossilised skulls of our distant relatives. They believed it was probable that we evolved from ape-like ancestors and were very much smaller, with longer arms and more body hair than we have today. However, recent research suggests that pre-human apes that walked on two legs had evolved by four million years ago.

Religion and Belief

People have always searched for explanations about life. Religion is a set of beliefs that tries to explain the aspects of life we do not fully understand. There have been and still are a number of different religions in the world – those whose followers believe in many gods and others whose followers worship just one god. Today, the main religious groups are Muslims, Christians, Hindus, Buddhists and Jews.

Humankind

One of the last species of mammals to appear on the planet, we are the most successful and dominant alive. Our intelligence has made us capable of incredible achievements; we are the only primates to have developed oral language and technology. We have an insatiable thirst for knowledge and our understanding of the world and universe about us grows as our species evolves.

As HUMANS, WE ARE BY far the most numerous and successful of all the primates. In the last 300 years, our population has grown from about 1,000 million to nearly 6,000 million. Because we have intelligent, reasoning minds and opposable thumbs, we have been able to make and use tools and have created a reading and writing system that allows us to communicate in astonishingly complex ways. Through science and technology we are able to make sense of the world about us. It has taken us four million years to gain all the skills necessary to bring us where we are today.

More than any other animal, we feel a need to be creative, to express an awareness of ourselves and our surroundings. We have invented tools and devices that help us live our lives as fully and with as much enjoyment as possible.

MOST PRIMATES HAVE LARGE BRAINS AND ARE HIGHLY INTELLIGENT.

Everyone is unique and individual in their interests, which is why we have philosophers, politicians and computer experts, athletes, painters and mountaineers.

We are capable of feeling and expressing a vast array of emotions, from inconsolable grief to immense joy. We have huge capacities for compassion and empathy and mostly

Humans live all over the planet, from the freezing polar regions to the scorching deserts of Africa.

strive to improve life. However, we are also more destructive than any other species alive.

MOTHER TERESA

There are many outstanding people who have dedicated their lives to others; Mother Teresa is one of them. Born Agnes Gonxita Bojaxhiu in a village in Skopje, Macedonia, she joined the Catholic Order of Our Lady of Loreto in 1929 and went on to become one of the best-loved and most well-known workers for the underprivileged on the planet. She became known as 'Mother Teresa' and as the Dalai Lama said, was 'a towering embodiment of the power of love, her great compassion an inspiring example of the true essence and potential of spiritual life.' Mother Teresa was awarded the Nobel Peace Price in 1979. She died in 1997.

HUMANS ARE ALL MEMBERS OF ONE SPECIES CALLED 'HOMO SAPIENS'.

War, conflict and argument are part of our daily lives as we struggle to understand and communicate with other humans. Our attempts to live alongside the rest of the animal kingdom are no better; rather than treat them with respect, we often try to own or control them.

THE HUMAN BODY IS A COMPLEX COLLECTION OF MORE THAN 50,000 MILLION LIVING CELLS.

People and Science

We constantly ask questions about our environment: how things are made, why things happen the way they do, where things come from or go to. As a result of this inquiring existence, we have been able to discover all sorts of answers, such as: what the tiniest particles are that make up the universe, how to light our homes with electricity, how to cure diseases, and how to make gadgets to make our lives easier. One of the greatest and most inspirational achievements of humankind was the space voyage of 1969 when Neil Armstrong became the first person to walk on the moon.

Deer

Winter Coats

Our winter anoraks and jackets are often filled with light, airy padding. Heat travels very slowly through still air, so our body heat finds it difficult to escape and keeps us warm instead. A deer's winter coat works in exactly this way. Each hair on its body is hollow, like a small sealed tube, trapping the air to keep it warm. The hair also acts like a life belt in case the deer needs to swim.

Nimrod

Thousands of years ago, in Mesopotamia, lived a king called Nimrod. He had twin sons. Out hunting one day, Nimrod's sons met a beautiful horned doe (female deer) whose antlers glittered with light. They chased the doe for two days until she jumped into a lake and disappeared. In sadness, Nimrod's sons built a temple by the lake and lived in it for five years.

Reindeer Facts

Reindeer live in the vast stretches of icy tundra across the top of the world. A reindeer oddity is that it has a loose tendon, which slips over the anklebone, making a loud clicking sound as the animal walks.
The reindeer is the only species in which both males and females grow antlers. A baby reindeer's antlers start to grow at three weeks.

DEER ARE CREATURES of paradox – graceful, sensitive and gentle yet also very determined to follow their own paths. Deer have an amazing ability to stand very still, often camouflaging themselves against their surroundings. There are many tales of deer luring hunters deep into the forest and then simply 'disappearing' into the trees.

THERE ARE ABOUT 36 different types of deer and they are found on every continent. Different species have adapted to all climates from tropical to polar.

The most obvious characteristic of deer is their pair of antlers, which only the males possess. Antlers are covered with a fur called velvet, which supplies blood to the antlers as they grow.

LIKE ALL DEER, CARIBOUS ARE HERBIVORES. THEY EAT LEAVES, LICHENS AND FINE TWIGS.

Once a year, adult males fight with their antlers to decide which of them will mate with the females. During the fight, called the rut, the males roar loudly. Deer shed their antlers each spring and grow new ones in time for the next rutting season.

For centuries, deer have been hunted but they have developed many ways to survive. When in danger, the sika deer fluffs up the patch of white fur on its rump. This is a warning signal to other deer.

White-tailed deer are shy animals that do not usually congregate in large herds.

CHINESE WATER DEER ARE THE ONLY DEER NOT TO HAVE ANTLERS.

In summer, the fallow deer has white spots on its coat, which provide a clever camouflage against leaves and branches.

A deer has an excellent sense of hearing. Instead of moving the whole of its head, it swivels its ears to locate the sound. This enables it to listen while feeding and also to know immediately from which direction the sound is coming and flee. A deer's whole survival depends on the sensitivity of its ears.

Musk deer have special glands under their stomachs, which produce a smelly substance, called musk, during the breeding season.

THE FAWN'S SPOTS

When the first ever fawn was born, its mother was nervous. All around her, watching from the shadows were fierce animals that preyed on the young and the weak. So she prayed to the Great Creator to find some way to protect her child with its weak and wobbly legs. The Creator put down his work and came. He made the fawn a shirt of soft doe skin, dabbed with the colours of the brown earth and the black fire charcoal and added some white, yellow and just a touch of red saying, "as long as the fawn wears this and keeps still, he will be invisible to all his enemies." From that day onward if a fawn remains absolutely still, it is camouflaged by its dappled coat.

Many have been hunted and killed to obtain this gland, which is then used to make perfume.

The male pampas deer has similar glands on his hooves, which give off a strong garlicky smell that can be detected 1.6 km (1 mile) away.

THE ELK, OR MOOSE, IS THE LARGEST OF ALL THE DEER.

The Long Trek

In Alaska and northern Canada, reindeer are called caribou. The caribou of Canada make the longest migrations of any land mammal. Their young are born in the high tundra of the Arctic during the summer months and then, in the autumn, herds of up to 20,000 deer move south 1,125 km (700 miles) to the edge of the forest region. In the summer they go back north, a round trip of 2,250 km (1,400 miles).

King of Benares

An old Indian story tells of two herds of deer – led by two golden stags named Branch and King Banyan – living in a royal park. Each day the King of Benares visited the park and killed many of the deer. Unhappy, the stags decided that every day the deer should draw lots. Whoever drew the lot would be sacrificed to save the others. One day, the lot fell on a pregnant doe. King Banyan graciously offered to die in her place. When the King of Benares heard this he was so touched he never hunted the deer again.

Hare Council

The hares were afraid. Surrounded by enemies – men, dogs, beasts and birds of prey – they lacked courage to go on. So they called a council and at length decided they would all kill themselves. As the hares rushed towards a nearby pool to drown themselves, they frightened the frogs, which jumped into the water and hid beneath lily pads. The hares were so pleased to find a creature that was actually frightened of them, they decided to live on a little longer.

Hare Tales

The children's tales of Brer Rabbit come from the West African belief in the hare as a trickster. The hare was also seen as a trickster by the plainsmen of North America. If you meet a hare it is generally considered to be unlucky and if one crosses your path, it is best to go home again.

Story of Snowshoes

Snowshoe hares have thick white hair on their feet to stop them from sinking into the snow. One story tells how the hare got his snowshoes. When the world was young and Michabou the mighty hunter fought the Spirit-Bear to see who would be king of the north, the hare helped the Spirit-Bear by stealing Michabou's snowshoes as he lay sleeping. When Michabou woke he could no longer walk across the deep snow, but sank. In the end he grew tired and gave up the battle. As a reward, Spirit-Bear let the hare keep the snowshoes.

Rabbits and hares

ALTHOUGH RABBITS AND HARES ARE members of the same family, rabbits have been domesticated and bred as family pets but hares have always remained wild. They both have huge hind limbs, which make them swift runners, and chisel-shaped teeth, which grow throughout their lives. Rabbits and hares are often seen in meadows at dusk and because of this are often linked with the moon.

RABBITS AND HARES have some very different physical characteristics. The hare is much larger than the rabbit, having a body length of 52-60 cm (20-30 in) to the rabbit's 40 cm (16 in). Its ears are much larger and its hind legs more powerful.

Most of a hare's and a rabbit's body heat is lost through its ears and the size varies according to whether the animal lives in a hot or cold climate. The jackrabbit of Arizona, USA, has very large ears, whereas the ears of the Arctic hare are small.

IF SNOW HAS COVERED THE GROUND AND THERE IS NO GRASS TO EAT, RABBITS EAT TREE BARK.

Rabbits can be found anywhere as they burrow out their homes and tunnels in the earth. Their burrow system is called a warren, where up to 30 rabbits live in a group. Baby rabbits, called kittens, are born blind, deaf and hairless in a side burrow lined with their mother's fur.

Their eyes open at 10 days and at 18 days they start to play outside. Rabbits are very alert to danger and can even be startled by their own shadows. Their huge ears help them pick up even the smallest of sounds.

AS AN ALARM SIGNAL, RABBITS THUMP THEIR HIND FEET HARD ON THE GROUND.

Hares are more solitary than rabbits and live in more exposed countryside. They do not burrow but live in forms. A form is a shallow bowl that the hare scrapes in the ground among long grass.

Rabbits and hares have a good defence instinct. When a shadow passes by, they can freeze in an instant, avoiding the keen eye of a bird of prey flying overhead.

SOME RABBITS HAVE UP TO 30 BABIES A YEAR.

Easter Hare

The pagan goddess of spring was the hare-headed Eastre. Her favourite animal was, naturally, the hare and it was the first animal to be linked with the Easter festival. Later the rabbit became linked too. A bird called a plover lays its eggs in an empty hare's lair. German children are told the Easter hare lays the Easter eggs they receive each year.

BREEDING RABBITS

In 1850, British settlers took six rabbits to Australia. The rabbits bred and spread out across Australia at the rate of 110 km (70 miles) a year. By the end of the century, rabbits had changed the face of Australia, eating most of the shrubs and grasses and leaving much of the countryside looking like a dust bowl. Ranchers put up fences to keep the rabbits out but there were so many of them that when they came to a fence, those at the rear climbed on the backs of those at the front and clambered over the fence! In 1950, Australians introduced the terrible rabbit-borne disease myxomatosis to kill the swarming rabbits and give the grasses a chance to grow again.

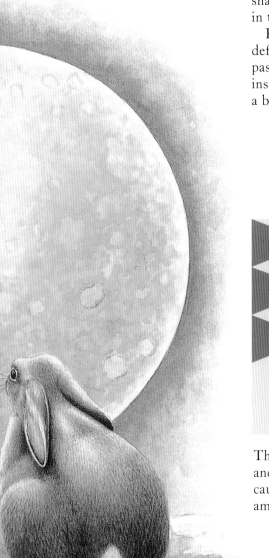

They can also run rather fast, and double back to avoid being caught – a hare can run at an amazing 70 km/h (45 mph).

ARCTIC HARES AND SNOWSHOE HARES GROW WHITE FUR IN WINTER TO BLEND IN WITH THE SNOW.

Hares and rabbits come out of their forms and burrows just as the moon is rising and spend a few hours frolicking around as the night draws in.

Hares and Witches

During the Middle Ages it was thought a witch could change into a hare and if a hare was wounded then a witch would be found with a similar injury. In fact, one woman accused of witchcraft in 1662 recited at her trial; "I shall go until a hare, With sorrow and such meikle care. And I shall go in the Devil's name, Ay when I come home again."

Rats

RATS HAVE LONG been seen as enemies of humans. Many people dislike the sight of them as they often carry diseases. The bubonic plague that spread across Europe in the 1300s and killed 25 million people, a quarter of the population of Europe, was brought by rats travelling in the holds of ships from the Black Sea to Genoa.

Blind Leading Blind

In 1924, a miner noticed two rats walking, one slightly behind the other, each holding one end of a piece of straw in its mouth. After watching for a while, he realised that the second rat was blind and was being led by the first. A naturalist, taking part in the BBC's *Living World* programme, reported that he had seen two rats walking along, one holding the tail of the other. When he examined the rats, he found that the tail-holding rat was blind.

Rats can become serious pests, devouring huge quantities of crops.

THERE ARE MORE THAN 50 species of wild rat, living in most terrain from damp places to deserts.

Most rats use burrows but some live in buildings and some even live in trees. Rats will eat almost anything and can gnaw their way through most materials. Their diet includes birds' eggs, rubbish, dead animals and farm crops. In one test at the Public Health Service Laboratory in

RATS' FRONT TEETH STAY PERMANENTLY SHARP.

Savannah, USA, rats chewed through a panel of foam glass 5 cm (2 in) thick and a panel of aluminium 1.25 cm (0.5 in) thick.

Rats have a strong family urge and female rats will adopt almost any animal given the chance. Experiments have shown that they will adopt baby mice, rabbits, kittens and even chicks.

WHEN A RAT IS RELAXED IT GRITS ITS TEETH.

Rats are very intelligent. In fact, they are almost as intelligent as dogs and need the company of a social group. They are not often puzzled by the same obstacle twice. Rats are genetically very adaptable and some populations have even become immune to the poison warfarin, put down to kill them. Now some rats need to eat warfarin regularly just to survive.

Mice

Like rats, mice are rodents or 'gnawing animals'. They have no canine teeth and there is a wide gap between their incisors and molars so that the incisors can be used for gnawing, nibbling and carrying. These teeth never stop growing so rodents need to wear them down by gnawing.

ALTHOUGH EQUALLY adaptable to their surroundings, mice are more cautious than rats. A mouse will use his whiskers to measure a space before he tries to squeeze through. Mice are constantly alert to danger, scampering swiftly and silently from one piece of cover to another but, if faced with an enemy, they have tremendous courage, despite their size.

The harvest mouse is so light it can climb a wheat stalk without breaking it.

THE MOUSE AND THE GIRAFFE HAVE THE SAME NUMBER OF NECK BONES – SEVEN.

Like rats, mice breed at an astonishing rate. They are mature at 10 to 12 weeks and a single mouse may have 30 or 40 young in the course of the year. If these all survive and have children themselves, a pair of mice could be ancestors of a million offspring in two years.

WHITE TAME MICE ARE DOMESTICATED VARIETIES OF WILD MICE.

Mice and rats may live in dirty places but they keep themselves clean, stopping to groom their coats regularly, even when hunting. They are good housekeepers and store up food for the future.

The common house mouse is about 10 cm (4 in) long with a tail of around 11 cm (4.5 in) and lives in houses, barns and similar places. The tiny harvest mouse is only 6 cm (2.5 in) with a tail about the same length.

Dormice easily fit into the palm of a hand. They live mainly in hedgerows but as they only come out at night, it is not likely that you will often see one.

Strong Mice

The word 'muscle' comes from the Latin word, *musculus*, meaning 'little mouse'. If you hold one arm out straight, palm up, clench your fist and then bend your arm up and down at the elbow, you should be able to see the biceps moving about like a little mouse under your skin.

SUPER MOUSE

H.C. Hahn, a biologist from Texas, USA, tells the story of a brave mouse. Once, while on a wildlife trip, he saw a snake climbing a tree with a field mouse in its mouth. As he watched, suddenly another mouse ran up the tree and jumped on to the snake's back, sinking its teeth in and hanging on. Unable to attack the second mouse as it still had the first in its mouth, the snake dropped its prey and turned on the hero. As soon as the second mouse saw that its companion had been released, it leapt off the snake's back, escaping just before the snake had a chance to strike again, and ran for safety with its mate.

Ant Bodyguards

Some black ants act as bodyguards for the caterpillar of the imperial blue butterfly. Each morning, the ants leave their underground nests and climb wattle trees to join the caterpillars as they eat the leaves. The ants use their strong jaws to drive off any predators, while the caterpillars feed. In return, the ants get to suck a sugary secretion from the caterpillars' backs.

Circular Milling

When ants are on the march or attack, sometimes those on the edges of the columns get cut off from the others. They seem to lose their direction, then begin to go round in circles. Hundreds or even thousands of ants continue this circular milling for days until they die.

Leaf-cutter ants carry home leaf pieces to their nests to help cultivate the fungi they use for food.

Ants and termites

BOTH ANTS AND termites are extremely social animals – in one nest there can be several thousand ants or termites. The welfare of the group is put above that of each individual and throughout their lives most ants and termites work very hard, each member of the group having its own particular job to fulfil. Co-operation and industry are very important to these little creatures.

ANTS LIVE IN HIGHLY organised colonies consisting of winged males, wingless females (called workers) and fertile females (called queens). Male ants have wings and short antennae and their only job is to mate with the queen. Once they have done this they die. Queens do not work, but breed to produce offspring for the colony. Most worker ants carry out their role without ever stopping for a rest, collecting materials for nest building and food for the rest of the group.

THERE ARE AT LEAST 10,000 BILLION ANTS IN THE WORLD.

Ants can carry many times their own size in weight and if the item they find is too heavy for them, they will drag it or get help from other workers. If an obstacle is in their path, they will either march over it, round it or even take it with them.

Some ants have slaves to do some of the work for them. The British red ant and the European Amazon ant raid the nests of black ants.

WOOD ANTS BUILD MOUNDS OF PLANT DEBRIS THAT CAN REACH 1.5 M (5 FT) HIGH.

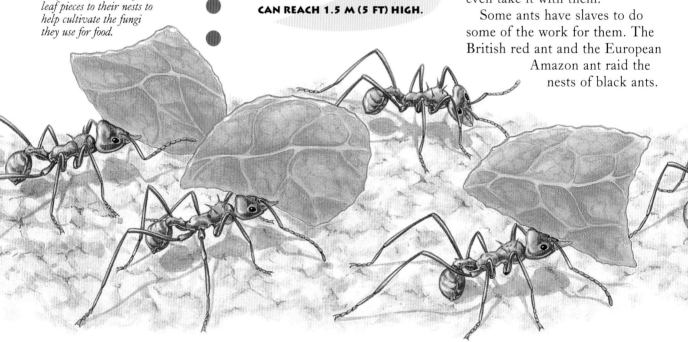

The central royal chamber, where the queen lays her eggs, is at the heart of a termite mound.

They carry off the pupae to their own nests. When the new ants are born, they become slaves.

Some ants keep their own 'cattle' – tiny aphids or greenfly which produce a sticky substance called honeydew.

The ants herd the aphids together and 'milk' them.

In the autumn, the ants collect the aphids' eggs and watch over them until they hatch in the spring. Then the ants carry the aphids above ground to allow them to suck the sap from plants and so produce some more

honeydew. When the plants start to wilt, the ants move the aphids to new plants, just like the farmer moves his cows to new pasture!

THERE ARE AROUND 2,000 SPECIES OF TERMITES IN THE WORLD.

Most termites are the size of a grain of rice and almost blind. They live in colonies, just like ants, with the queen laying up to 36,000 eggs a day. When the colony is big enough, the queen starts to produce winged males and females that fly away to start new colonies.

Termites build high-rise dwellings called termitaries. Inside these pillars of soil cemented with saliva and baked by the sun, are layers of rooms, galleries and passageways with ventilation and drainage. In some parts of Africa and Australia, termitaries reach 6 m (20 ft) high and are 3 m (10 ft) in diameter. Each one is home to around three million termites.

Which Way?

Dr. Felix Santschi, a zoologist, demonstrated that ants navigate by observing the position of the Sun. First he covered travelling ants with lightproof boxes so that they were completely in the dark. Then he removed and replaced the boxes intermittently. Each time the box was removed, the ants set off on a different course, altered by the degree to which the sunlight had moved while they were kept in the dark.

Leaf-cutter ants have huge jaws that operate like shears as they slice the leaves into manageable pieces for transport.

MEXICAN ARMY ANTS

Some ants will eat their way through anything. Mexican army ants, although blind, divide into columns to encircle their prey. Now ants are on the march in Brazil – but these are not ordinary, 'eat-anything-that-gets-in-the-way' ants. These ants have developed a taste for the protective gel that coats computer circuit boards. They are also partial to televisions, telephone circuitry and anything else that contains a computer circuit board. Some ants even ate through the wiring of the world's largest superconductor while it was still under construction and short-circuited the system. So keep crumbs away from your computer – they might attract ants.

Air

· · · · · · · · · · · · · ·

HUMANS HAVE ALWAYS dreamt
of flying unaided and in this
chapter we meet the creatures that
make it look easy. From the tiniest
ladybird to the awesome bald eagle,
the air is home to a huge variety
of animals. Their grace and beauty
in the sky has meant that birds, in
particular, have often been associated
with power and freedom. Here we
explore the symbolism and legends
that surround these creatures, as well
as their amazing survival strategies
and extraordinary abilities.

THE LARGEST FLYING CREATURES
IN HISTORY WERE PTEROSAURS. THEY
LIVED 70 MILLION YEARS AGO.

FEATHERS ARE MASTERPIECES
OF NATURE – LIGHT YET WEIGHT-
BEARING AND INSULATING.

BIRDS AND BATS USE THEIR TAILS
AS AIR-RUDDERS, TURNING THEM TO
CHANGE FLIGHT DIRECTION.

Hanging Out

A bat hooks the curved claws on its hind feet around a support and hangs head downwards. In this position, its toes automatically grip the support without slipping. This is because the toes are pulled by tendons, which are stretched by the weight of the bat's body. Even if the bat falls asleep, it will not fall off. In this position, a bat has a good view of what is going on around it and its wings can be spread ready for take off!

Chinese Bats

In China, the bat is a symbol of long life and happiness, bringing with it five-fold blessings of wealth, health, virtue, old age and a natural death. Fu-Xing, the Chinese god of happiness, is often shown as a bat.

There are about 130 different species of fruit-eating bats. They search for fruit in trees using their keen sense of smell.

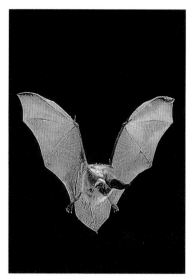

Bats

BATS ARE THE only true flying mammals. Their wings have very similar bones to the arms and hands of humans, with skin stretched between their long finger bones and bodies to form the wing membrane. As well as for sustained flight, bats use their wings as blankets while they sleep. Their legs are so weak they can hardly crawl, but their strong wings help them to take off into a fast flight from a flat surface.

THERE ARE NEARLY 1,000 species of bat in the world. In fact, one species in every four mammals is a bat. Like all mammals, bats have hair or fur on their bodies, are warm-blooded and, when babies, feed on their mother's milk.

Insect-eating bats are mainly nocturnal, whereas fruit bats fly during the day or at twilight.

TWENTY-FIVE PERCENT OF ALL MAMMALS ON EARTH ARE BATS.

When insect-eating bats fly, they send out high-frequency squeaks, mostly inaudible to humans. The returning echoes give them information about what is ahead, including the size and shape of an object, whether it is moving and, if it is, in which direction. This system of finding their way is called echolocation. When flying in groups, bats don't collide as each responds to its own echo-signals.

THE WORLD'S SMALLEST BAT IS THE HOG-NOSED BAT AT 3 CM (1.25 IN) LONG.

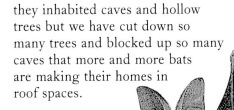

Many bats eat insects. The tiny pipistrelle bat can eat 300 mosquitoes in an hour. Bats pollinate flowers, live in our houses and fly daily in our evening skies, yet few people see them.

Bats don't make nests but find cosy nooks and crannies in which to live. At one time they inhabited caves and hollow trees but we have cut down so many trees and blocked up so many caves that more and more bats are making their homes in roof spaces.

Pipistrelle bats roost in groups of up to a thousand or more, in lofts, churches or farm outbuildings.

THE LARGEST FRUIT BAT HAS A WINGSPAN OF MORE THAN 1 M (4 FT).

However, the biggest gatherings of mammals on Earth are still found in the caves of southern USA where Mexican free-tailed bats live in colonies of up to 30 million. Bats that live in colder climates find a quiet place free from disturbance, such as a crack in a rock, and tuck themselves away to hibernate during the winter. They go into hibernation with round, fat stomachs full of food, which keeps them alive through the winter. In spring, they emerge very thin and have to find more food quickly to build up their strength.

Vampire Bats

Western belief has always linked bats with vampires – undead spirits that prey on the blood of the living. In the Middle Ages in Europe, people thought bats sucked blood from sleeping children. A vampire bat has four razor-sharp canine teeth with which it collects the blood of other animals, usually horses, and shares it with other bats. Bats starve very quickly so this 'food-sharing' saves their lives.

Immortality

As bats lived in caves, which were seen as entrances to the next world, they were thought to be immortal and so became symbols of immortality. In parts of Africa, Australia, Bosnia, Tonga and England, the bat was sacred because it was believed to represent the soul of the dead. Some people even believed that if you touched a bat, your soul would be able to travel at night.

WHITE LADY

Leonard Dubkin, a naturalist, wrote affectionately about the bats he studied. One, called White Lady, once flew straight through an electric fan rotating at the rate of 800 revolutions a minute, without being damaged. Once, as a tiny baby, it was hanging from Dubkin's finger when its mother flew past, grabbed it off the finger and carried it away without pausing. When White Lady was grown up, to test its homing instinct, Dubkin drove 144 km (90 miles) from his house and released it in an area it had never seen. When he got home, White Lady was already there.

Bee Sting

The queen bee is the only bee with a retractable sting. If a worker stings, it leaves the sting in its victim's flesh and dies. A story from ancient Rome tells how a bee took some honey as a gift to the god Jupiter and Jupiter offered the bee a gift in return. The bee asked for a sting to protect her honey from humans. Jupiter loved the human race but had made a promise, so he said, "You shall have your sting but at peril of your own life. If you use it, you will die from the loss of it."

Bees collect pollen and store it in pollen sacs on their back legs.

Bees

First appearing on the planet 146-174 million years ago, bees have been around on Earth three times longer than the Rocky Mountains, USA. In ancient Egypt, the bee was said to have sprung from the tears of their sun god, Ra. In fact, bees do take directional guidance from the sun. The bee has also been seen as a giver of life because, although it disappeared in the winter, it returned each spring.

EACH INDIVIDUAL honeybee is part of a colony of thousands in the beehive. The focus of each hive is the large queen bee, which lays up to 3,000 eggs a day. To maintain the energy to do this, she eats 80 times her own weight every 24 hours.

BEES SUCK UP NECTAR FROM FLOWERS THROUGH THEIR LONG, HOLLOW TONGUES.

Most of the other 20,000-40,000 bees in a hive are workers, females with various tasks. Some are nurses feeding protein-rich bee milk to the queen and the

Each cell of honeycomb is six-sided.

larvae. Some workers make wax, eating honey that is converted by special glands into beeswax, then chewing the wax and moulding it into six-sided honeycomb cells.

The cells hold the stores of honey, pollen or the young larvae.

FLYING BEES BEAT THEIR WINGS 180 TIMES PER SECOND AND FLY AT A RATE OF 35 KM/H (22 MPH).

Other workers go out to find pollen and nectar, which they give to the honey makers to store in the combs. The older bees act as hive guards. The average life span of a worker bee is just seven to eight weeks. Males, or drones, exist only to mate with the young queens and then they die.

Wasps

LIKE BEES, social wasps, which live in colonies, are either queens, drones or workers. Solitary wasps, which live alone, are simply males or females. The most common wasp, with its yellow and black body, is a social wasp. It lives in nests made from papery material.

IN EARLY SUMMER, the queen starts a nest by building a few six-sided cells of a comb and laying eggs in each. The nests are made by chewing wood from trees and fences and mixing it to a pulp with saliva. Once the little grubs hatch out, the queen feeds them fruit and flower juices, then whole pieces of fruit or caterpillar.

Unlike the queen bee, the queen wasp works from dawn to dusk.

THE SPIDER-HUNTING WASP OF SOUTH AMERICA IS 63 MM (2½ IN) LONG.

Finally the grubs change into pupae and produce workers that continue to build the nest into a home for many more. These wasp nests have rows and rows of neat cells, like a block of flats. Workers clean out each cell as soon as it is empty, ready for the queen to lay another egg.

Wasp drones are not idle either but share in the work of the nest, cleaning out cells and moving the bodies of dead wasps or grubs. As soon as the colder days of autumn arrive, all the grubs that are left are taken from the cells and killed. This seems cruel but it saves them from a lingering death,

as workers will no longer be able to find food for them. The first frosty night kills the workers and the drones die soon after. Only the queens, hiding in hollow trees or under loose bark, live to start a

ONE WASPS' NEST CAN EASILY BE HOME TO AROUND 5,000 WASPS.

new colony the following year. Some species of wasp are more likely to sting than others and generally, smaller wasps are less aggressive than larger ones.

Usually a wasp will only sting to defend the nest or if it feels threatened. When a wasp is protecting the nest it flies with a wing beat frequency that rouses other wasps, encouraging them to fly around and attack the intruder.

In summer, wasps are drawn to rotting fruit. They use it as a substitute for nectar, chewing with their powerful mouthparts.

Solitary Wasps

Solitary wasps can be divided into those that use a nest and those that don't. Nest building females construct a few separate cells or dig small holes in the ground and lay one egg in each, next to a paralysed insect, which is food for hatched larvae. Others lay their eggs in the paralysed prey so that when the larvae hatch, they can eat their way out of their home.

THE BEE WOLF

The bee wolf is actually a wasp. Mostly yellow in colour, the female bee wolf digs an amazing series of tunnels and nest cells in sandy soil, doing most of the digging with her front legs. She lays an egg in each cell and seals the doorway with soil. Within three days, the eggs hatch and the larvae start eating. She feeds her larvae on honeybees, three to six of each of the 15-20 cells. Two weeks later, their food supply used up, the larvae spin a bottle-shaped cocoon and settle down to turn into bee wolf wasps. When they hatch, the wasps have to dig their way out of their cells and into one of the tunnels that leads to the exit from their underground home.

Passionflower

In the tropical forests of Central and South America, a battle is going on between a butterfly and a vine. The heliconus butterfly lays her eggs on the passionflower vines. When the larvae hatch, they eat the vine leaves. To save themselves, the vines try to fool the butterflies into thinking they are not vines but other plants, by varying the shapes of their leaves. However, the butterfly is not so easily taken in. When it lands on a leaf, it drums its legs up and down to test if the leaf actually sounds like a vine leaf.

Moon Madness

Some moths use the Moon like a compass to guide them, so light bulbs and candles will easily distract them. You can often see moths flitting around streetlights. Sometimes a moth may even flutter into a naked flame by mistake and burn up.

Too Clean

The pale version of the grey peppered moth is well camouflaged against lichen on trees and walls. In the 1860s, a black version of the moth appeared. On soot-covered trees and buildings of industrial cities, the dark version was better camouflaged than the original form and became common as it was less likely to be eaten by birds. As city air becomes cleaner and lichens flourish once more, the pale version is becoming more common again.

Butterflies and moths

IN THE DAYS of your great-grandparents, summer gardens would have been busy and bright with butterflies and moths, living jewels of colour, flitting from flower to leaf. Today, the sight of a butterfly or moth is more of a surprise. Modern farming methods have taken over flower-strewn meadows and hedgerows, where butterflies and moths used to feed.

IN CHRISTIAN, CHINESE, Greek, Italian and Mexican mythology, butterflies and moths are symbols of life after death, due to their fascinating life cycle from caterpillar to chrysalis to winged creature. The Chinese linked butterflies with the Plum Tree of Life and they often buried their dead with jade amulets of carved butterflies.

BUTTERFLIES CAN TRAVEL UP TO 1,000 KM (600 MILES) WITHOUT STOPPING.

When you look at a beautiful butterfly or moth, there seems no obvious connection between it and a caterpillar. However, it is the slow-moving caterpillar that turns into this delicate, winged creature – one of the most extraordinary transformations on our planet.

The eggs of a butterfly or a moth hatch into caterpillars, which start eating straight away.

THE ANTENNAE OF A MALE MOTH CAN PICK UP THE SCENT OF A FEMALE 8 KM (5 MILES) AWAY.

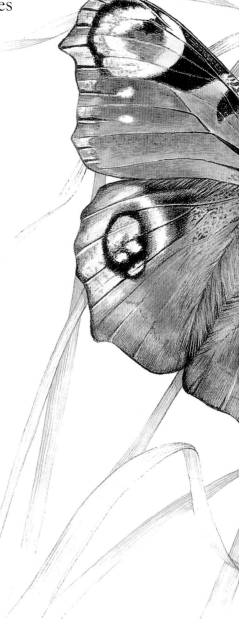

They munch away for weeks, growing larger and larger and they shed their skins several times. When the caterpillar has reached full size, it ties itself to a twig or leaf stem, using silk, and slips off its last caterpillar skin to reveal a chrysalis.

Most moths and butterflies make silk, which is produced in short lengths by their salivary glands. The caterpillar glues

MOST BUTTERFLIES AND MOTHS DON'T EAT FOOD, BUT JUST DRINK TO SURVIVE.

these threads together to make a cocoon to protect itself during the chrysalis stage. The ermine moth builds a lacy net container, while the moon moth builds a chrysalis with a silver sheen.

From the outside, a chrysalis looks lifeless, a dead thing hanging from a branch. But inside something amazing happens. Part of the caterpillar dies, but other tiny cell clusters grow. Slowly, the growing cells form a new body. One day, the cocoon splits, a head with two huge eyes appears, then legs and finally a butterfly or moth crawls into the world.

Moths and Butterflies

If you see a moth in the daytime, it is probably a butterfly! Generally moths fly by night, butterflies by day. Butterflies are brightly coloured, while moths' colourings tend to be duller. When a butterfly rests, it holds its wings upright over its body but a moth spreads its wings out or folds them over its back. If you get close enough to see, a moth's antennae are feathered or pointed, while a butterfly's are club-shaped.

ANT AND THE BUTTERFLY

An ant, running in the sunshine, came across a chrysalis that was near its time of change. The ant looked at the dry, shrivelled cocoon and scoffed. It boasted how it could run where it wanted, climb a tree if it wished, while the chrysalis could only lie imprisoned in its shell, unable to do anything. A few hours later, the ant passed that way again and found only an empty shell where the chrysalis had been. Suddenly, the ant felt a cool breeze and there above him, fanning its wings, was a beautiful butterfly. "You can boast to me as much as you like now," said the butterfly and flew away leaving the ant far behind.

A newly hatched butterfly spreads its wings out in the sun to dry before it flies off.

Moths' wings usually blend in perfectly with the habitat in which they live, making them difficult to see.

Insects

Beetles

Beetles have long been viewed with superstition. The scarab, or dung beetle, was sacred to the ancient Egyptians and was often carved on gemstones or amulets. The scarab takes fresh dung, rolls it into a ball with its front and back legs and then trundles it backwards until it comes to a spot where it digs a hole and buries the dung. The female then lays her eggs inside. Because the ball was the same shape as the sun and the beetle moved its ball the same way as the sun moves across the sky, the Egyptians adopted the beetle as a symbol of life and resurrection.

Jumping Fleas

A flea can jump 130 times its own height – that's the same as a human jumping to the top of a 70-storey building! To achieve these incredible leaps, fleas have to accelerate with a force 20 times greater than the force required to launch a space rocket. They can also jump 350 times their own body length. That's like a human jumping the length of a football field.

Flies Eyes

Like all insects, flies have compound eyes – eyes that consist of numerous separate light-sensitive units. Each unit has its own lens so flies and other insects see objects as a mosaic of overlapping points of light. Flies cannot focus sharply on objects, but pick up the slightest movements around them.

AT LEAST THREE-QUARTERS of the known animal species are insects – that's more than one million for every human on Earth. Insects were the first creatures to fly. The earliest known insects had two pairs of wings that did not fold and could be flapped alternately, like dragonflies' wings today. The bodies of insects vary greatly in size – from less than 0.25 mm (0.01 in) to 25cm (10 in) – and in shape, but they all have a head, thorax and an abdomen.

NOT ALL INSECTS FLY. An acre of pastureland contains around 360 million insects, most of which are wingless, leaping insects.

The thorax of an insect is divided into three parts, each of which has a pair of legs. Insects breathe through their abdomens by means of tiny air holes, which lead into tubes, called trachea, along which air travels around the body. Insects eat in two ways: by sucking or chewing. If they have jaw-like 'mandibles' then they chew their food. If they have a tube-like 'proboscis', like a butterfly, they suck their food.

THE FIRE BEETLE OF AUSTRALIA CAN WALK THROUGH RED-HOT ASHES.

Flies can walk on almost every surface, even upside down on the ceiling. This is because each of their feet has a pair of hooks and two pads covered with tiny, sticky hairs. But they don't just use their feet for walking. Bluebottles taste sugar through their feet, which are covered with sweet-sensitive taste buds.

They can taste traces of sugar millions of times more efficiently than the human tongue. Ichneumon flies can even hear and smell through their feet. Mayflies never eat as they don't have mouths but they only live for two to five hours or a few days at the most. The daddy-longlegs is so sensitive to warmth that the touch of a human hand may kill it.

SOME TINY MIDGES BEAT THEIR WINGS 50,000 TIMES A MINUTE.

The dragonfly is the state insect of Alaska, USA, and was chosen to represent the area because, according to the Governor of Alaska, "the dragonfly's ability to hover and fly forwards and backwards reminds us of the skilful manoeuvring of the bush pilots in Alaska." In fact, a dragonfly can outdo any pilot as it can stop dead at 56 km/h (35 mph), fly

Ladybirds have two sets of wings – a hard outer pair protects a soft inner pair.

FLIGHT MUSCLES WORK WELL IN WARM CONDITIONS – SOME INSECTS CAN'T FLY IF IT'S TOO COLD.

backwards and make very sudden turns. Like all flies, dragonflies have compound eyes and can spot food 37 m (120 ft) away. They fly with their legs together to form baskets in which to capture insects that they eat while still in the air.

The skeletons of insects are on the outside of their bodies and other body bits are often in unexpected places. A locust's ear is in its abdomen, while a daddy-longleg's ears are in its feet.

HOVERFLIES HAVE STABILISERS BEHIND THEIR WINGS SO THEY CAN HOVER PERFECTLY STILL.

Dragonflies are one of the few insects that have not changed much since prehistoric times.

Ladybirds

There are male and female ladybirds. Underneath their hard outer wings, they have paper-thin flying wings, which they flap nearly 100 times a second as they fly. Ladybirds eat aphids and other plant-harming insects. One story says that in the Middle Ages, plagues of insects were eating the crops. The people prayed to the Virgin Mary for help and a swarm of ladybirds came and ate the pests, so they called the little bug 'beetle of Our Lady'.

Little Leapers

There are more than 20,000 kinds of grasshoppers and crickets. The chirping sound they make is produced by the rubbing together of the rigid veins on their front wings or by rubbing part of the back leg against the wing vein. If you want to know how hot the weather is, count the number of chirps a cricket makes in 14 seconds, add 40 and the result is the temperature in Fahrenheit.

River Fly

A legend from eastern Canada tells how, when the world was new, there was a beautiful river. Fish swam in it, beavers built lodges in it and all the animals came to drink there. Then a great moose came along and began to drink the river dry. Everyone was worried but nothing they said or did persuaded him to go away. Then the fly promised to get rid of the giant moose. The animals laughed, "You! You're so tiny!" Fly said nothing but when the moose appeared, he landed on the moose's nose and bit it sharply. Then he jumped all over the moose, biting and biting until eventually the moose could stand it no more and ran away.

Owl Eyes

Owls have huge eyes that can hold a fixed stare. They have a third eyelid, which moves from side to side to clean their eyes and clear their vision. An owl's pupils can contract or expand quickly to adapt to light conditions but its eyes are fixed in one position, so it must turn its whole head to look around. One of the owl's eyes is set higher than the other. This helps it to judge accurately how far away an object is.

Pellets

Owls eat their prey whole, so much of what they eat cannot be broken down by their digestive systems. An owl regurgitates this part of its meal but first the bones, hair and feathers are all squashed together to form pellets. By examining owl pellets, naturalists can discover what owls eat.

Owls

Because it can see in the dark and looks thoughtful and serious, in ancient cultures the owl was taken as a symbol of wisdom, seeing through the darkness of ignorance. In modern western culture, the owl is also linked with ghosts and dark forces. This is probably because owls usually fly at night, flitting about silently and letting out occasional mournful hoots.

Owls are short-tailed, soft-feathered birds with big heads and enormous eyes. Their beaks are hooked and partially hidden by feathers.

MOST OWLS CAN HEAR SOUND TEN TIMES SOFTER THAN A HUMAN EAR CAN.

Lords of the night, most owls hunt after dark. With eyesight a hundred times sharper than ours, an owl can see through the leaves and overhanging branches to the forest floor, where mice and voles scamper about. As soon as owls see the tiniest movement below they swoop down and grab the small creature in their claws, killing it with their sharp, hooked talons.

Owls vary in shapes and sizes, from one that is so small it lives inside a desert cactus, to the great horned owl, which is the only bird of prey that can outfly the golden eagle.

OWLS' WINGS ARE FRINGED WITH SOFT FEATHERS TO MAKE THEIR FLIGHTS ALMOST SILENT.

The barred owl makes its home in swamps and dense woods, while the burrowing owl gets its name because it either digs its own burrow or takes over the abandoned tunnel of the prairie dog.

The eastern screech owl is also called the 'shivering owl' and the great horned owl, a fierce hunter, has been nicknamed the 'tiger of the night'.

THE ELF OWL, AT ONLY 15 CM (6 IN) LONG, IS ONE OF THE SMALLEST OWLS IN THE WORLD.

Among the larger species of owls are the eagle owls, which look as if they have pointed ears sticking up on the tops of their heads. These are just tufts of feathers and are not connected to their hearing at all. The northern hawk owl, found mainly in Canada, North America, northern Asia and Scandinavia, deviates from owl rules as it is the only owl to hunt by day rather than by night. In flight, it looks a little like a hawk, with its short pointed wings and unusually long tail.

Owl Ears

Roger Payne, a student at Cornell University, USA, placed an owl in a large wooden shed. The shed was sealed so no light could enter and the floor was covered in leaves. In pitch darkness, Payne released a live mouse. As soon as the mouse rustled in the leaves, the owl left its perch. Payne turned on the light just in time to see the owl with the mouse in its talons. When Payne plugged one of the owl's ears, the owl was unable to find the prey in the dark.

Twit-Twoo

The owl's hoot has many superstitions attached to it. An old English belief was that the screech owl only called when rain was on the way. In some areas of rural France it is thought that if a pregnant woman hears an owl hoot, she will have a baby girl. In ancient Rome and in Celtic lore, an owl that hooted at the time of death was believed to be waiting for the soul of the dying person.

In ancient Rome, the owl apparently appeared at the deathbeds of several emperors, and the death of a queen was foretold by an owl alighting on her house.

When hunting, a barn owl flies 2-4 m (6.5-13 ft) above the ground.

The snowy owl lives in the tundra regions of the Arctic and has a wingspan of about 1.5 m (5 ft) and often hunts during the day.

SWIFT AND SILENT

One report tells the story of a man who loved owls. Every morning he fed a wild great grey owl that had a wingspan of around 1.5 m (5 ft). One morning the man was outside collecting stones to put in a tank with some frogs. He picked up three grey stones and was holding them in the palm of his hand when suddenly they were not there anymore. All he had in his hand was a bright red gash, oozing blood. Faster than he could blink and more silently than he could imagine, the owl had swooped down, grabbed the stones and was already sitting on a branch about 2 m (6.5 ft) away.

Storks

AN ODDITY OF THE bird world, the stork – with its white feathers, long legs and strange walk – has been the source of many superstitions. In western countries, the white stork is said to bring new babies to parents. This legend may have begun because storks are seen in and around water and water is traditionally associated with fertility. It may simply be because storks take good care of their young.

Mother Love

Once, a thatched roof on which a stork was nesting caught fire. The stork sat over its young to protect them and beat at the flames with its wings. When the fire was extinguished, the stork was black with soot and smoke burns but at least its children were safe.

Mother storks are very protective animals. On hot days, they have been seen carrying water in their bills to give their young a drink.

Storks are sociable birds and don't mind living alongside humans.

STORKS ARE LARGE, long-legged wading birds with elongated necks, long broad wings and webbed feet. They are strong

THERE ARE 17 SPECIES OF STORK LIVING THROUGHOUT THE WORLD.

fliers and look particularly striking in flight with their necks and legs stretched out, legs hanging down slightly.

When members of a breeding pair meet, they perform a greeting ceremony by clattering their bills. They feed mostly on frogs, reptiles, insects and molluscs.

White storks live in Europe and western Asia during the summer and migrate south to Africa in the winter. They often nest on top of trees or houses. Once a nest is made, it is used and added to year after year. Over the years a nest can grow into a cylinder of twigs 1.8 m (6 ft) high and 1.2 m (4 ft) wide. In the nest, the female lays between one and five eggs, which both parents incubate.

THE OPENBILL STORK HAS A GAP IN ITS BILL, WHICH ONLY MEETS AT THE TIP.

Cranes

Cranes are large, graceful birds that can be found on five of the world's seven continents. South America and Antarctica are the only places they do not inhabit. Cranes are one of the most threatened bird species and, of the 15 types of crane, 11 are in danger of becoming extinct.

SPLENDID-LOOKING, with brightly coloured bare skin on their faces and decorative plumes on their heads, cranes are aggressive birds. When a crane is fighting another crane, it leaps into the air to stab at its opponent with its bill or rakes it with sharp claws. The fighting continues until one bird flies or runs away, sometimes closely pursued by the victor. A running crane takes one to three steps per second and may use its wings for balance and speed. Cranes can easily outrun humans.

Eurasian cranes and sandhill

THE LARGER SPECIES OF CRANE STAND AT 1.5 M (5 FT) TALL.

cranes prepare themselves for the breeding season. They preen themselves by rubbing mud into their feathers. The Siberian crane rubs it into its neck too. This helps to camouflage them in the marshlands but it also helps them to attract a mate.

Cranes are good swimmers, although they do not have webbed feet. Chicks follow their parents into the water within hours of hatching. A chick in distress calls for its parents in a high-pitched peep, while adults call to each other with a soft purring.

After breeding, cranes fly in large flocks in a V-formation or in a line to warmer climates.

Crane Dance

Cranes migrate in the winter. In the spring, when they return, they perform a wonderful mating dance. Hornborgar Lake, in Sweden, has become a tourist attraction as people flock there each spring to see around 70,000 cranes dancing. In some countries, traditional dancers copy the movements of the crane and add them to their dances.

Whooping Crane

The cry of the whooping crane sounds like an Indian war cry. The world's population of whooping cranes is less than 250 and they are in danger of disappearing altogether. Their one breeding area is in Wood Buffalo National Park, Canada. Cranes like privacy and, although Robert Parker Allen was appointed to protect and conserve whooping cranes in 1943, it was not until 1955 that he and his team actually found where the cranes were hiding.

KUNG FU

The art of Kung Fu is an ancient Asian form of self-defence, which uses quick body movements to evade and retaliate at the same time. Many years ago, an old man was sitting by a pond, thinking and watching a crane, when a gorilla came out of the forest and attacked the bird. The old man was sure the crane would be killed but was amazed at how the crane avoided and defeated the ape. Cranes dodge about to confuse an attacker and gracefully use their wings to parry blows and sometimes catch an attacker's blow at an angle that throws it off balance. They also use their claws as weapons. The 'White Crane' style of Kung Fu imitates these actions.

Two-headed Eagle

Some countries have used the symbol of a two-headed eagle to show they are all-powerful and are watching everywhere. The Middle Eastern Hittites carved it on monuments, then it appeared in Byzantium. Later, in 1155, Frederick Barbarossa, king of the Romans, chose it as a symbol for the Holy Roman Empire. Finally, it was adopted by Ivan III of Russia in 1472.

Legions of the Eagle

Ancient Persians and Romans going into battle carried eagle standards as symbols of their power and bravery. Every French regiment in Napoleon's army carried a bronze standard in the form of an eagle. Eagles were painted on to many shields during the Crusades and they are also one of the many emblems of chivalry.

Fancy Feathers

Eagle feathers are used around the world on clothing, ceremonial tools and headdresses. In Native American lore, a headdress made from eagle feathers symbolises the Thunderbird, the Great Spirit, and the feathers carry the prayers of the tribe up to the sky.

Eagles

EAGLES FLY AND nest higher than any other birds and so were once thought to converse with the gods. They have entered our hearts and imaginations as creatures of power, inspiring awe and perhaps sometimes a longing to join them in the skies. Often seen as a king of birds, this bird of prey has always been a symbol of royalty, authority, strength, victory and pride.

ALTHOUGH NOT THE swiftest of birds, the eagle has captured human imagination. Its wings are an engineering marvel, not only powerful enough to carry it high and far but also with feathers that act like wind-flaps to increase lift, reduce turbulence and prevent stalling at low speeds. When an eagle spirals upwards towards the sun, it is in fact coasting downhill on rising air.

AN EAGLE'S EYESIGHT IS EIGHT TIMES MORE POWERFUL THAN A HUMAN'S.

It rises because the upward-moving air is travelling faster upward than the bird is travelling downwards, rather like someone walking down an upward-moving escalator. Its wings are not designed for speed, but for soaring.

There are 59 species of eagles worldwide. Groups of bald eagles gather by rivers near the Alaskan coast, where they prey on fish.

EAGLETS (YOUNG EAGLES) HAVE TO BE TAUGHT HOW TO HUNT AND KILL.

Bald eagles breed in northern North America on inland lakes and sometimes migrate to the south to find food. Pairs stay together year to year and engage in elaborate courtship displays by locking talons mid-air and somersaulting down together. They make their nests of sticks in large trees or on rocks and add to it year after year. One of the largest eagles in the world is the golden eagle, which measures about 90 cm (3 ft), from the tip of its beak to the tip of its tail and

The bald eagle is far from featherless but has a paler cap that covers its head.

has a wingspan of about 2 m (7 ft). When hunting, the golden eagle soars for long periods, using its incredibly sharp eyesight to scan the countryside, then diving down to seize an animal. It uses its powerful back talon to kill the prey, while its front three grip the animal securely. Golden eagles build large, untidy nests in tall trees or on rocky ledges and these can be 1.8 m (6 ft) in diameter.

EAGLES KILL WITH THEIR CLAWS AND USE THEIR SHARP BEAKS TO CUT THROUGH FLESH.

Despite the power of its beak and talons and the fierceness of its eye, the eagle has a very weak voice that is almost a chirp.

Like eagles, vultures are birds of prey too, but they scavenge the leftovers of other animals.

Bald Eagle

The bald eagle was adopted by the USA in 1792 as the national emblem. It appears on coins and paper money and is symbolic of power and strength. In the emblem, the eagle's wings are outstretched to show its power but its foot rests on an olive branch to show that power is sheathed in peace. The bald eagle is not bald but has a white head. The word 'bald' comes from the old English 'balde' which means 'white'.

EAGLE SNATCHER

One tale tells of a woman whose baby was snatched by an eagle. The baby had been wrapped in a shawl and laid to sleep in a corner of a harvest field, where his mother was working. The eagle, which was nesting high on a nearby cliff, could be clearly seen flying back home with the baby in its mouth. The cliff was very steep and no one had climbed it before but the desperate mother ran after the bird and somehow managed to climb up to the nest. In it she found the baby, alive and unharmed, still wrapped in the shawl. She snatched the baby from under the eagle's beak and climbed shakily back down the cliff.

Parrots

PARROTS ARE fascinating tree-living birds. Their colourful plumage and engaging behaviour makes them one of nature's great attractions. From the largest macaw to the tiniest budgie, members of the parrot family are known as hookbills because of their short, powerful and strongly-hooked beaks.

Scarlet macaws fly off noisily at the slightest disturbance.

Talking Birds

Parrots can talk. Until recently it was thought that their 'speech' was just sound mimicry but more recent research has shown they can interpret some of what is said to them. It seems they can learn spoken phrases and identify symbols. Dr. Irene Pepperberg of the University of Arizona, USA, works with African Grey parrots. Alex, the oldest parrot, can identify five shapes, seven colours and over 100 objects. It also knows many phrases and when to use them.

of the parrots. At home in the rainforests and Savanna of South and Central America, they are seen less and less in the wild because of the destruction of their natural habitat and because so many of these birds are caught to be sold as pets. Macaws form strong pair bonds and in the spring adults scream for a partner. They nest in holes in trees and as they make their daily trips to the feeding grounds, pairs fly together, wings almost touching.

TO CLIMB UP TREES, PARROTS USE THEIR CURVED BEAKS AS WELL AS THEIR CLAWS.

PARROTS ARE found over the warmer parts of the world, from the rainforest regions of America and Africa to Australia, New Guinea and the Solomon Islands.
In the wild they are graceful birds.
Macaws are among the most beautiful and flamboyant

PARROTS CAN LIVE FOR BETWEEN 50 AND 70 YEARS.

Parakeets are fairly small, sociable parrots. They are extremely noisy and are usually seen in small flocks, although they may gather in their hundreds at feeding sites. Seeds, berries, fruit, flowers and nectar are their usual food. Monk parakeets build nests at the beginning of the breeding season. At first they only have a few compartments but are gradually added to until there are up to 20, each inhabited by a pair of birds.

Toucans

A MONG THE MOST extraordinary birds in the world, toucans live in the dense rainforests of the Amazon region of South America. A toucan's boldly coloured beak makes up almost half of its body length and its plumage is usually dark with contrasting colour on its head and neck.

Snappy Eater

If you have ever tried throwing peanuts or sweets and catching them in your mouth, then you have been imitating a toucan. A toucan seizes its food with the tip of its bill, throws its head back and tosses the item into its mouth. Toucans enjoy playing with their food in the wild and often toss it high into the air and then fly up to catch it!

All Sorts

There are 42 kinds of toucan, ranging from birds 33 cm (13 in) to birds 63.5 cm (25 in) long. Although they all have large bills, these differ in size and style from species to species. The curl-crested aracari has jagged notches on its blue-striped beak. The plate-billed mountain toucanet has a horny yellow plate that grows from each side of its upper bill, while the emerald toucanet has yellow and black stripes along the length of its bill.

PROBABLY THE MOST well-known toucan is the large toco toucan. Toco's plumage is mainly black and white with a few red tail-feathers. Its golden bill is about 9 cm (7.5 in) long and you might think it would overbalance when flying but the bill is lighter than it looks. Like all toucans, it feeds on fruit and has a great liking for passion fruit and peppers. Tocos are not at all shy and will come into houses and steal food if given the chance.

THE SHY EMERALD TOUCANET LIVES AT AN ALTITUDE OF UP TO 3,000 M (10,000 FT).

The toco toucan lives in small groups and likes to visit coconut and sugar plantations.

Toucans nest in holes in trees either made naturally or abandoned by woodpeckers. If a hole is not big enough, a toucan enlarges it by pecking away at the trunk with its beak, letting the wood chips fall to the ground to make a soft base. Its nest is usually about 30-61 cm (12-24 in) deep to make room for its large beak.

A female toucan lays two to four eggs. Both parents then look after and incubate the eggs.

A TOUCAN'S TONGUE IS NARROW WITH BRISTLES AT THE TIP AND LOOKS LIKE A FEATHER.

After 15 days the chicks will hatch, but they are born without feathers and they're blind until about three weeks of age.

TOP OF THE BILL

Toucans eat mainly soft food, such as small fruits, although their bills are hard enough to dig into tree trunks in search of insects. Their remarkable beaks are constructed of a light, horn-like material called keratin. Inside, the bills are hollow and honeycombed with a network of struts, which keeps them light for flying but also gives them strength. The beaks have saw-like edges, which enable the birds to tear off large pieces of fruit. The reasons for such a large beak are not clearly understood. However, toucans sometimes use their bills to 'fence' with each other in play and the brilliant yellow colour is probably used to attract mates.

Symbol of Peace

The dove has been seen as a sacred bird and a symbol of peace since ancient times. It is the one creature into which neither the Devil nor a witch can change themselves. To Christians, the dove is a symbol of the 'Holy Spirit'. In Roman mythology it was thought to be the messenger of Venus, the goddess of love.

Final Tribute

During his life, Captain Joseph Belain of the US Navy spent a great deal of time and effort working to save the carrier pigeon service from falling into disuse. When he died, his burial service was held in a church. During the service, a carrier pigeon flew in from the sea and sat on the coffin until it was over.

Dove Tail

Each pigeon wing contains 20 flight feathers. When they are spread, the feathers overlap each other without any gaps. In the ancient Greek myth of Jason and the Argonauts, Jason was rowing across the sea when he came to a narrow channel. The only way through was to navigate the 'Symplegades', clashing rocks that moved around in the sea, crushing ships as they passed through. Jason released a dove, which flew through the channel, losing only its feathers as the rocks crashed together. This enabled Jason to judge the time it would take for him to row through the passage.

Pigeons and doves

DOVES AND PIGEONS belong to the same family of birds. Descended from the wild rock dove, they have been domesticated for centuries. The ancient Egyptians kept them as long ago as 3000 BC. Although all originally from one species, years of selective breeding have produced many types and sizes of domestic pigeon.

MANY VARIETIES OF WILD pigeons and doves can be found in all parts of the world except very cold regions. If you walk in the woodlands, you might hear the cooing of pigeons or be startled by the loud flapping of their wings as they leave their nests. The wood pigeon and stock dove make their nests in trees or holes in trees while the rock dove nests in holes in the cliffs of wild, rocky coasts!

If they are not using holes to nest in, pigeons and doves build little rafts

THE PASSENGER PIGEON WAS HUNTED TO EXTINCTION IN THE 1800S.

of twigs and sticks with a slight hollow in the centre for their eggs. Pigeons usually lay two eggs at a time and newly hatched pigeons are strange-looking little creatures. Blind and helpless, they have bluish-black skin and no feathers, just a few tufts of yellow down. The parents feed the young birds with a curd-like white 'milk' from a part of their throats called the

Some people place dovecotes in their gardens as houses for pigeons.

crop. When pigeons first leave their nests at around 23 days old, they can't fly.

Pigeons are a familiar sight in city squares the world over. Perhaps the most closely linked to humans are the carrier pigeons.

PIGEONS ARE THE ONLY BIRDS THAT CAN SUCK – OTHER BIRDS JUST SIP AND SWALLOW.

Pigeons have a strong instinct to fly home to the place where they roost or were bred, and have an ability to do this over a long distance. They navigate using various information sources, such as the Earth's magnetic field, movement of the sun and stars, wind direction and cloud movements. Because of these homing instincts, pigeons are ideal messengers and for most of our history they have been able to fly faster and more directly than any other means of transport. Carrier pigeons can fly at speeds of 48-97 km/h (30-60 mph).

THE FIRST PIGEON POST WAS STARTED IN AD 1150 BY THE SULTAN OF BAGHDAD.

Pigeons were used as messengers during World War I and II. It was a Japanese officer who first noticed that all Chinese sailing ships had pigeons aboard and that if the birds were released in the morning, they always returned to the ship at night. The officer experimented by releasing racing birds from mobile lofts and found that the pigeons returned to the lofts wherever they were.

In World War II, the British army dropped boxes of homing pigeons by parachute behind enemy lines. They were used

by resistance fighters to send messages back to London, UK.

Pigeons are naturally afraid of the loud noise of gunfire so it's amazing that so many of them flew through artillery, shrapnel and machine-gun fire, as well as through gas, fog and rain to deliver messages.

Racing pigeons are also popular. In Belgium their flying abilities form the basis for a national sport. A racing pigeon can fly at around 97 km/h (60 mph) or even more with a following wind. Different types of birds are used for different distances. Light birds are sprinters - they can fly fast in short bursts – but the larger ones are used for long-distance flight. Under good conditions, pigeons can fly for 13 hours non-stop.

Carrier pigeons are homing pigeons. They have excellent navigational skills and return home after delivering messages.

Red Feet

An Arabian legend tells the tale of how the pigeon got its red feet. After the world was flooded, Noah released the dove from the Ark. When it returned with an olive branch in its beak, Noah knew that the treetops were appearing and the floods receding. Noah released the bird for a second time and again it returned but with red mud on its feet. This showed that the dove had been able to land on dry land. Noah asked God if the dove's feet could forever be red to remind humankind of the time the world flooded.

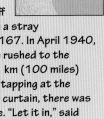

LOYAL PIGEON

In 1939, Hugh Perkins, the son of the sheriff of Summersville, West Virginia, USA, took in a stray carrier pigeon. He gave the bird the number 167. In April 1940, Perkins was taken seriously ill and had to be rushed to the nearest hospital, which was at Philippi, 161 km (100 miles) away. One night in the hospital, there was a tapping at the ward window. When the nurse drew back the curtain, there was a carrier pigeon tapping its beak on the pane. "Let it in," said Hugh, "I bet its mine. See if the number 167 is on its leg." The nurse opened the window and the bird flew in and perched on Hugh's bed. When he checked, the number was 167!

Birds of Ill Omen

Large black birds have often been linked to the Devil in folklore and are seen as omens of death or bad luck. To the Romans, the raven's cry of 'cras cras' meant 'tomorrow, tomorrow' and so was a symbol of hope. To the Christians, ravens were an emblem of God's providing, because ravens fed the prophet Elijah. Saints were often drawn with ravens beside them.

Ravens in the Tower

The raven is supposed to be able to see into the future and to smell death from a distance. There are always ravens at the Tower of London, in the UK, supposedly to protect Britain against invasion. Legend has it that if the ravens leave the Tower, Britain will fall to an enemy.

Crows and ravens

CROWS AND RAVENS belong to the same family and are among the most intelligent of the birds. They have amazing memories, are good at solving puzzles and like to collect shiny objects. They are adaptable birds and good opportunists, able to change their habits according to the new situations in which they find themselves.

RAVENS ARE ABOUT a third larger than crows, with a heavier beak, which is long and slightly hooked. They have more fan-shaped tails than crows and their plumage has a bluish, satiny sheen. Sometimes ravens have a ruff of feathers around the throat. They spend the winter in flocks but nest alone in tall trees or on cliff faces.

CROWS EAT INSECTS, SPIDERS AND SMALL MAMMALS BUT SCAVENGE FROM REFUSE.

THE CROW FAMILY INCLUDES MAGPIES, ROOKS, RAVENS AND JAYS.

The carrion crow is about 47 cm (19 in) in length and its plumage is all black. Hooded crows with their grey bodies and black heads, wings and tail, are a distinct species of the crow family.

Rooks are slightly smaller than crows and have longer, thinner beaks with a bare patch of skin between the eyes and shaggy, loose feathers on the thighs. They are more social than crows and if you see a flock of birds near a colony of untidy nests in a group of trees, then they will be rooks, not crows. Rooks are useful to farmers because they eat insects and worms that damage crop roots.

A GROUP OF RAVENS IS CALLED A MURDER.

Crows and rooks seem to be interested in watching how other animals behave. They sometimes tease or annoy other creatures by pecking or pulling their tails. They have learned that by doing this, they can distract an animal long enough to steal its food. Crows and ravens are also good at imitating sounds and have been known to copy words. Ravens can imitate other birds, falling water and even mimic music. Jim Nollman, an author, naturalist and pioneer in the field of interspecies communications, tells of a raven that joined him on a camping trip.

Crows can move fast on the ground as well as in the air.

The raven sat beside him for an hour; while Nollman played a Jew's harp, the raven croaked a low imitation of the sound, like a slower version of a cat purring.

ROOKS' NESTS

Strict rules apply in a rookery and if younger birds try to build a nest some distance away from the main rookery, older birds will destroy it. Legend has it that rooks have 'parliaments' where judgements are passed. One lady wrote of seeing a pair of young rooks build a nest further along her driveway from the rookery trees. Three times the older rooks destroyed it and three times the younger rooks rebuilt it. One day the disobedient pair were encircled and flown to a nearby meadow. After much cawing, the mass of rooks rose in the air and started to peck the culprits as a punishment.

TAME ROOKS CAN LEARN TO IMITATE HUMAN SPEECH.

The Clark's nutcracker, a North American member of the crow family, buries pinecones as food stores and can remember up to 3,000 different hiding places. Ravens don't like people to see them hide food. If they think they are being watched they dig it up and hide it again.

During the nesting season rooks gather in large communal roosts, called rookeries, to breed.

Raven Fortune-teller

The raven is seen as a shapeshifter (one that can change its body) and an omen of change. In Norse mythology, the god Odin relied on two ravens for news of the world. They sat, one on each shoulder, and were called Huginn and Muninn (Mind and Memory). In days of old, the magical emblem of the Danish standard was the 'Fatal Raven'. Its wings would move to forecast results of a battle. If the wings hung down, the Danes would be defeated but if they were spread, then victory was certain.

Water

WATER COVERS MORE than two-thirds of our planet and provides a home to millions of creatures, from the familiar animals that live and play on the riverbanks to the extraordinary organisms that dwell in the deepest seas. The darkest depths of the ocean remain the world's last real wilderness and we are still discovering the amazing animals which live there.

MILLIONS OF YEARS AGO, LIFE BEGAN AS MINUTE BACTERIA IN THE WORLD'S WATERY ENVIRONMENT.

OVER 500 VARIETIES OF FISH HAVE SPECIAL DISC-SHAPED CELLS THAT CAN PRODUCE ELECTRICITY.

THE ANTARCTIC PROVIDES THE OCEANS WITH OXYGEN-RICH WATER TO SUPPORT A VAST ARRAY OF LIFE.

The Great Change

Salmon are often seen as fish from the 'Other world', able to change from one form to another. One Irish folktale tells of a soldier who laughed that the salmon was held in such awe. He vowed to catch it and eat it for his supper. He did catch one but when he took out his knife, it turned into a beautiful woman. Also in the Celtic legend of Tuan MacCarell, the magical qualities of the salmon are kept alive. Tuan comes to Ireland as a salmon, is captured and eaten and reborn as a man.

Salmon

IN MANY CULTURES salmon are considered to be magical and inspirational fish. This idea has probably grown out of the tremendous changes salmon go through during their lives. After growing up in the sea, the Pacific salmon begins an heroic journey home to its birthplace in a small stream, to breed and lay its eggs. Once this journey is complete, the salmon's body changes rapidly and ages at an amazing rate. In a few days the salmon dies and its young begin their arduous journeys through life.

Again and again the salmon jumps up rapids and waterfalls, using its strong and flexible body to reach home.

THE SALMON IS at home in both saltwater and freshwater, and can be found all over the world. A salmon lays its eggs in the gravel bed of an inland stream. When the baby salmon hatch, they are only a fraction of a centimetre (inch) long and feed off the food stored in their mother's yolk sac. Some months later, the still tiny salmon follow their instinct move downstream to the broad, deep river until finally they reach the sea.

WHEN CARRIED BY THE CURRENT TO THE SEA, SALMON GO TAIL FIRST.

Out in the vastness of the Pacific and Atlantic Oceans, it is only the strongest of the salmon that survive. Between one and five years later, the fish that was once the size of a sardine, now 45 cm (18 in) of gleaming silver, begins the great journey home.

Somehow the salmon finds its way from the oceans to the exact spot in the quiet stream where it was born. All the way back is upstream, against the current, so the salmon must use all its strength to push on and not be swept back to sea. It keeps going, not stopping to eat and avoiding fishing vessels sweeping the mouths of rivers with their nets.

FISH LADDERS HELP SALMON AVOID DAMS AND OTHER BARRIERS ON THEIR JOURNEYS UPSTREAM.

It must also look out for animals such as grizzly bears, otters and mink on the lookout for a fish supper.

As if that isn't hard enough, the salmon has to jump up rapids and waterfalls. It can jump a waterfall 3 m (10 ft) high in one leap but at a larger fall looks out for rocky ledges, and leaps up in stages. The salmon may fall back several times but it won't give up – something stronger than weariness and the need to rest drives it on and it struggles on to its destination.

Like a warrior who battles to overcome obstacles and dangers on its quest, the salmon struggles and endures, using its strength and determination to swim back, perhaps thousands of kilometres (miles) to where it began.

IN ANCIENT BRITAIN, THE SALMON WAS GUARDIAN OF WELLS, POOLS AND STREAMS.

At last the salmon reaches its home ground where it chooses a mate who has made the same journey. Here, where its own life began, its young are born to start their own adventurous journeys through life.

Salmon Power

A Dakotan Indian chief had a beautiful daughter. He sent out a challenge that whoever was strong enough to break the pair of elk's antlers that hung in his lodge could marry his daughter. All the animals and birds tried but their strength and skill were not enough. The only creature left was the salmon. He broke the antlers into five pieces and, claiming his prize, led the beautiful daughter away.

Little Helpers

Sighted salmon have been seen guiding blind salmon by swimming close to them and pushing them in the right direction. One pair was seen to have a code; a push near the tail meant turn right and one near the head, turn left.

SALMON ADVENTURE

A salmon, taken from a hatchery in Humboldt County, California, USA, was released into a coastal stream 9 km (5.5 miles) away, to see if it could return to the tank in which it was born. After swimming up a small stream and under a large highway, the salmon reached a sewer. Here it went up 24 m (80 ft) to a small water channel. At the end of the channel was a 10 cm (4 in) drainpipe, which rose vertically 76 cm (2.5 ft). The salmon jumped up the drainpipe and into the outlet pipe that led to its tank. However, here it found that the outlet pipe had a cap on. After a few attempts, the salmon knocked off the cap and finally arrived back in the tank where it was born!

Blue-ringed Octopus

The blue-ringed octopus is just 10 cm (4 in) across but it kills more people in Australia each year than sharks do. However, it is shy like other octopuses and only attacks if it is picked up or disturbed. When it bites with its parrot-like beak, it kills its prey with poisonous saliva. The salivary glands produce enzymes called proteases, which partially digest food before it reaches the stomach.

Giant Squid

In the 1930s, the *Brunswick*, a 15,287 tonne (15,000 ton) tanker owned by the Royal Norwegian Navy was attacked three times by a giant squid. Each time the squid wrapped its tentacles around the hull and tried to pull the ship down. During World War II, a British Admiralty trawler was anchored in the Indian Ocean, near the Maldive Islands. One of the crew, who was standing on the deck fishing, saw a green, glowing light in the water. He realised he was looking into the eye of a huge squid. The sailor claimed that the squid lay alongside the 53 m (175 ft) ship, over-reaching it at either end.

Octopuses have more efficient eyes than humans because octopuses don't have a blind spot. They also have twice as many light-sensitive cells, so can probably see much more detail.

Octopuses

ONE OF THE MOST feared sea-creatures, octopuses have often been called devilfish. Many untruths about their fierceness are believed but in fact they are very shy animals and usually keep away from any animal larger than themselves. If frightened, an octopus may change from one colour to another, much as we might blush or turn pale.

OCTOPUSES FIND hidey-holes and manage to ooze their great bodies through the smallest gaps into empty clam shells, discarded bottles and cracks in rocks. They may stay in these tight spaces for weeks, returning to them after hunting trips, not always coming back from the same direction and making detours to avoid obstacles.

AN OCTOPUS HAS A RING OF EIGHT ARMS AROUND ITS MOUTH.

Octopuses are one of the most intelligent of invertebrates, able to make judgements in new situations. They learn from their successes and failures and apply what they learn to solve problems. This particularly applies to situations that need navigational skills and a good spatial memory.

Seahorses

ONE OF nature's most extraordinary creatures, seahorses are fish without scales – their bodies are covered with an armour of tough, bony plates. A seahorse swims with the body held vertically and propels itself along with a tiny, yellow-tinged fin on its back, fluttering it so fast it is almost invisible.

THESE LITTLE creatures have the arched neck and head of a horse, the grasping tail of a monkey and the chameleon's ability to change colour. Their eyes move independently so they are able to look in two directions at once.

WHEN SEAHORSES ARE BORN, THEY ARE SO TRANSPARENT THEIR HEARTS CAN BE SEEN BEATING.

There are more than 40 species of seahorse, ranging from 2.5 cm (1 in) to 60 cm (2 ft) in length. They live in almost every warm sea in the world and are found in a whole range of colours.

Seahorses wrap their tails around plants and change colour to match their surroundings.

One of the slowest moving life forms in the sea, most seahorses never move above 0.016 km/h (0.01 mph).

An unusual characteristic of the seahorse is that the male, not the female, incubates the baby seahorses. The male has a pouch like a kangaroo, in which the female lays her eggs. For 45 days he watches over his children-to-be until, one day, a minute but perfect seahorse pops out of the pouch, closely followed by another and another until hundreds drift towards the surface of the water like tiny bubbles.

STRUGGLE FOR SURVIVAL

Despite its wonderful ability to camouflage itself by blending in with the surroundings, the seahorse still has a struggle to survive. Each pair of seahorses produces thousands of young but on average only two of those babies survive to adulthood. Then, if they do avoid being caught by tuna fish, crabs, skates and rays, the seahorses have other hazards to face. Each time a storm blows up, their fragile bodies may be torn from whatever they are clinging to, battered in the waves, cast ashore or they may simply die from exhaustion. Should they escape all these dangers, the seahorses may well be caught to become pets in a fish tank.

Bubble Buoyancy

In its calm, slow-moving life, the seahorse has one thing to avoid – getting a puncture! The seahorse keeps afloat with an internal balloon full of gas. If just one tiny bubble of gas escapes this buoyancy bladder, the seahorse sinks helplessly to the seabed. There the seahorse must sit until it has made enough gas to fill up its tank and refloat itself.

Black magic

In ancient times, the Greeks thought the seahorse was capable of black magic. Wine with a seahorse soaking in it was a powerful poison and the ashes of a seahorse, mixed with honey and vinegar, were used as an antidote to other poisons. The Roman writer, Pliny, advised using seahorse ashes to cure baldness, skin rashes and the bite of a mad dog!

Turtles and terrapins

MOST TURTLES AND TERRAPINS, like their land-living relatives, tortoises, move slowly on land. Their bodies are not well supported by their legs, so much of their weight rests on the ground. Turtles and terrapins are 'at home' anywhere because they carry their homes on their backs. When threatened, most kinds of turtles can withdraw into their shells and are protected.

Turtle Rescue

In March 1991, a sailor from South Korea fell overboard a cargo ship. While in the water, the sailor kept afloat by holding on to a turtle's shell for six hours. When the sailor was rescued by another boat, the turtle was also hauled aboard. Here it was given a meal of meat and bananas before being returned to the sea.

Racing Turtle

Long ago, a rabbit and a turtle had a race. They crossed valleys and high hills, the rabbit running as hard as it could, but each time it passed the turtle it soon found the turtle ahead again. In the end, the rabbit was exhausted and the turtle plodded on and won. How? There was only one rabbit, but a different turtle at the top of each hill!

On land most marine turtles move by alternating movements of their limbs, as most four-legged animals do.

TURTLES AND TERRAPINS live in both freshwater and saltwater, on land near marshes, swamps and in forests. Like tortoises, they are reptiles that have an ancestry older than dinosaurs.

Turtles are usually bigger than terrapins, who can be kept as pets. Their skeleton evolved as a protective horny shell, the upper part of which is supported by the ribs and backbone. The largest turtle in the world is the leatherback turtle, which can grow to a weight of 360 kg (800 lb).

THE STINKPOT TURTLE GIVES OFF A BAD SMELL WHEN THREATENED.

Its flippers span up to 2.5 m (9 ft). Most female turtles lay their eggs and bury them in pits of sand or earth. When the eggs hatch, the young turtles dig their way out to the surface. The female green turtle travels hundreds of kilometres (miles), to the beach of its birth, to lay its eggs. Using its foreflippers, it sweeps away sand to create a hollow for its body.

Creation Story

Many tribal creation stories say that the Earth was born on the back of a turtle. The Native Americans refer to North America as Turtle Island because their legends say that when the world was covered with water, the turtle plunged to the bottom of the oceans and brought the Earth up on its back so that people could have a safe, dry home.

The turtle then lies over the hollow, its shell level with the beach, and digs a hole about 40 cm (16 in) deep beneath its tail. It lays the eggs in the hole and after covering them with sand, returns to the sea.

Two to three months later, the young turtles hatch, climb out of the hole and rush to the sea.

SOME RIVER TURTLES STAY UNDERWATER FOR MANY HOURS WITHOUT COMING UP FOR AIR.

Pond turtles hibernate in winter, burying themselves in specially built chambers in the riverbank.

Adelita, a loggerhead turtle, was tagged with an electronic signalling device by researchers at the University of Arizona, USA, then released into the sea on 10 August 1996, just off the coast of Santa Rosalita, a small town in Mexico. Adelita was only one of many tagged turtles and the purpose of the research was to show that turtles make very long journeys to the beaches where they want to lay their eggs. At New Year, Adelita was just north of Hawaii and by 31 July 1997 had arrived in Japan. She had completed a journey of 15,000 km (9000 miles) – a very long swim for a turtle!

SNAPPING TURTLES ARE HIGHLY AGGRESSIVE, SHOOTING THEIR HEADS FORWARD WITH SPEED.

Unfortunately not many survive. The houses and hotels on the beach fronts are usually brightly lit at night. This confuses the young turtles, who find their way back to the sea by light reflecting from the water, and they wander towards the shore lights instead.

Today, many turtle species are rare and have become protected species. They are hunted for their meat, hides and eggs or captured and sold as pets.

The Turtle House

A 'turtle house' is a place at the bottom of the ocean where turtles go to be cleaned by a variety of fish. The turtles turn up regularly and sit contentedly, flippers tucked under, eyes shut, while fish such as the surgeonfish, pick away at their shells to clean them. A turtle that is enjoying its grooming may stick its head straight up to let the fish know it wants its neck cleaned.

Shark Teeth

Sharks use their teeth to bite, tear and grind their food but they don't chew. Most sharks have more than four rows of teeth. The front row does all the work and, as the teeth wear down, a spare row rolls outward to replace them. Sharks get a new set of teeth approximately every two weeks. One shark may have up to 24,000 teeth in its lifetime.

Man Shark

Some ancient kings were shown in pictures as half human, half shark. The British Museum in London, UK, has bronze reliefs of the King of Benin shown in this way. The Trocadero, in Paris, France, displays statues of the Kings of Dahomey as sharks with scaled bodies. The former Fijian President, Ratu Sir Ganilau, was said to be descended from the shark god Dakuwaqa. After his death in December 1993, a boat carrying his coffin left Suva Harbour in Fiji accompanied by a school of sharks.

Remora

Despite their fierce reputation, sharks do have some friends who literally hang on and go everywhere with them. Remoras are tiny fish that attach themselves to sharks by means of suction pads on their heads. They earn their keep by cleaning parasites from the shark's skin. One shark may have two or more remoras on it, showing its status as a hunter who can provide free food for others.

Sharks

THE SHARK HAS been swimming in the oceans for 350 million years and its image as a vicious predator is written deep in the human consciousness. Its sense of smell is incredible – the shark can pick up and follow a scent as dilute as one part to 50 million parts of water. The shark is also sensitive to vibrations in the water and is particularly attracted by erratic movements.

SHARKS HAVE a reputation for killing humans yet fewer than 100 shark attacks a year are reported worldwide and most attacks don't cause serious injuries. The bull shark is one of the only sharks to come into shallow water and is responsible for many of the attacks on humans. Other dangerous sharks are the hammerhead, the tiger shark, the mako, the blue shark and the carpet shark. The carpet shark lies on the seabed looking so much like part of the ocean floor that swimmers may step on it by mistake and provoke an attack.

A GREAT WHITE SHARK CAN GROW UP TO 6 M (20 FT) LONG.

The great white shark is the most feared killer in our oceans. It is often called the 'white death'. Not many people ever see it as it rarely comes into shallow water where people swim.

Sharks have no enemies except other sharks and humans, although dolphins can kill sharks in some instances. It is true that sharks are efficient killing machines that have been evolving and adapting for some 400 million years. A shark can hear from an incredible 1.5 km (1 mile) away, smell and feel vibrations from 91 m (300 ft) and see from 27 m (89 ft). In fact, a shark can follow the smell of blood across huge distances in the ocean.

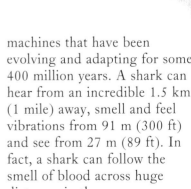

There are over 250 species of sharks and the numbers of many species are falling rapidly because of hunting and fishing by humans. Every day, 164,300 sharks are killed – that's 6,845 each hour, or two every second. Their meat is used for food, their livers for oil, the cartilage in health foods and other body parts in drugs and cosmetics.

Moses Sole

When Moses parted the waters of the Red Sea to let the Israelites cross, legend says a small fish was caught in the middle and flattened. Called the Moses sole, these fish give off a milky liquid which is an ideal shark repellent. The liquid from the fish is poisonous to sharks and paralyses them.

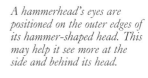

WHAT AN APPETITE

While dissecting a grey shark, vets found the hindquarters of a pig, eight legs of mutton, the front half of a dog and 136 kg (300 lb) of horsemeat in its stomach. Other reports tell how the crew of an old steamer fed one shark with newspapers, a biscuit tin, a brick wrapped in a piece of cloth, a sack of coal, a wooden crate and a broken alarm clock! Shoes, wallets, bits of other sharks, a driver's licence, dogs, a cow's hoof, the antlers of a deer, a chicken coop filled with feathers and bones and a chest of drawers have all been recovered from sharks' stomachs!

SOME SHARKS CAN DETECT BLOOD FROM 0.5 KM (0.25 MILES) AWAY.

A hammerhead's eyes are positioned on the outer edges of its hammer-shaped head. This may help it see more at the side and behind its head.

Six million blue sharks are caught annually by mistake, mixed up in the catches of deep sea fishing vessels. Sharks maintain the balance between the different fish species. When they are taken out of the sea food chain, many fish become scarce because they are eaten by other fish that were formerly eaten by sharks.

The great white shark has razor-sharp, triangular serrated teeth.

Whale Breath

Whales breathe air so, when they are below water, they must hold their breath. Some whales can hold their breath for up to 45 minutes. When they come up to take in more air, the air they breathe out is hot. As it hits the colder air outside it condenses into a column of vapour as much as 4.5 m (15 ft) high. This is what you see when a whale 'spouts'.

Sucking Fish

Sucking Fish, also known as the remora fish, challenged the whale to a race. The whale thought this hilarious and agreed. Grampus, the fastest swimmer in the sea, was to swim ahead and act as the judge but, just as the race started, Sucking Fish hid under Grampus's fin. When the whale arrived, Sucking Fish was already there. As a prize the whale agreed to carry him and to this day the remora fish travel attached to the whale.

The humpback whale has a curved lower jaw and approximately 22 throat grooves.

Whales

WHEN THE VOYAGER spacecraft travelled out to the stars carrying the message that life exists on Earth, many sounds of life on Earth were included: music, the sound of human voices, greetings in 60 different languages and the song of the humpbacked whale. Whale sounds span a broad range of frequencies, the lowest of which is well below the level that a human ear can pick up.

WHALES TALK TO EACH other using whistles and chirps. A blue whale's whistle can be 188 decibels – that's louder than the noise made by an aeroplane. The male humpback can sing non-stop for half an hour or more. Often members of a group sing the same song, repeating it note for note, beat for beat, exactly. Sometimes a group of whales leaves the winter waters and swims south in the middle of a song. When the group returns, six months later, it will pick up the song again as if there had been no interruption. The songs change and are added to month by month, year by year, as if the whales sing their own history as they make it.

An American biologist, Roger Payne, calculated that using the deep ocean sound channel, two whales making very low frequency sounds could

THE BLUE WHALE IS THE LARGEST MAMMAL EVER TO HAVE LIVED ON EARTH.

communicate with each other on opposite sides of the world.

For most of their history the whales, which don't have language as we do and don't have hands to signal, have communicated with

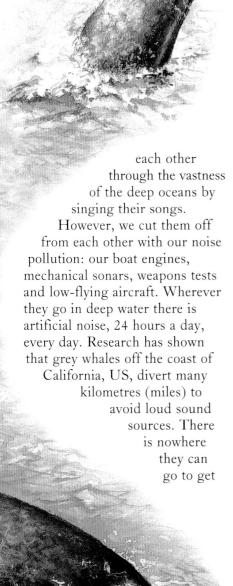

each other through the vastness of the deep oceans by singing their songs.

However, we cut them off from each other with our noise pollution: our boat engines, mechanical sonars, weapons tests and low-flying aircraft. Wherever they go in deep water there is artificial noise, 24 hours a day, every day. Research has shown that grey whales off the coast of California, US, divert many kilometres (miles) to avoid loud sound sources. There is nowhere they can go to get

THE MALE NARWHAL HAS A LONG SPIRAL TUSK GROWING FROM ITS MOUTH.

away from it, except shallow water, which may be why so many whales are found stranded on the beaches.

By sending out sounds and receiving back echoes from the objects around them, whales use echolocation to find their food, their way and each other. Sound and the force of a vibration are magnified underwater. For creatures with sensitive hearing that live in such a noise-polluted environment, it is very stressful.

In 1992, it was thought that whales found off Newfoundland, Canada, may have had damaged ear structures after underwater blasting was used in constructing oil rigs. Without their ears, whales are 'blind' and unable to communicate with the other members of their school. Many people and organisations are working to protect whales from such injury.

SPERM WHALES DIVE UP TO 1,000 M (3,300 FT) TO FIND FOOD.

STAR OF THE EAST

The *Star of the East*, a whaling ship, was sailing out near the Falkland Islands in 1891, when its crew spotted a whale. Two small boats were launched to harpoon the whale. In the struggle that followed two sailors went overboard. One was drowned and the body of the other disappeared. Eventually the whale was killed and cut open. Inside, they found one of the missing crewmen, James Bartley, unconscious but still alive. Amazingly, Bartley recovered from his ordeal, although it took some weeks, but his skin had been bleached white by the acids in the whale's stomach. It stayed that way for the rest of his life!

Whale Island

In many cultures the whale is said to support the Earth on its back and so when it moves, there are earthquakes. In Slav folklore, four whales support the Earth. There are also many popular legends of sailors mistaking a whale's back for an island, landing on it and lighting a fire to cook food. The whale, feeling the heat, plunges into the ocean and the sailors are drowned.

Whale Birth

Whales are born tail first. Like most mammals, they breathe air and if their babies were born headfirst they would drown. As soon as a baby whale is born, its mother and sometimes another whale, help it to the surface to take its first breath of air.

Dolphin Symbols

As long ago as 2200 BC dolphins appeared in cave paintings in Norway. The walls of the Aegean Palace of Knossos, in Greece, are covered with dolphin frescoes. All across the world, from the East to Asia and Western Europe, dolphin images have been found on coins, pottery and statues. Tales of dolphins are recorded in stories and songs. Roman coins dated 74 BC show a boy riding a dolphin.

Good Teachers

At the Society for Environmental Awareness in Key Largo, Florida, USA, dolphins play gently with children with severe learning difficulties, in seawater pools. After a session with dolphins, the children show greater interest in their surroundings and are often more creative afterwards. They also show improved communication, increased learning skills and positive behaviour changes after spending time with dolphins.

Dolphins

THE DOLPHIN IS NATURE's ambassador. Many times throughout history, dolphins have reversed the law of the wild and sought out humans, rather than fled from them. There are many recorded tales of dolphins saving humans from drowning, befriending them and then carrying them on their backs. Pliny, the Roman historian, tells of a wild dolphin that took a boy for a ride at Hippo, a Roman settlement in Africa.

WHY DO WILD DOLPHINS come into the bays and inlets of our shores to seek contact with humans? Why do so many people who meet dolphins talk of feeling love and friendship coming from the dolphins to them? Some people who work with dolphins believe that they give off an energy – the Japanese call it 'chi energy' – which rebalances and heals us. In ancient Greece, to kill a dolphin was a crime punishable by death.

Dolphins belong to the whale family and there are 32 different species. They are found in all the world's oceans and some rivers in tropical countries. Long and streamlined, their colourings and markings vary but dolphins have the familiar long beak and bulging forehead. Inside the bulge is a pad of fat called the 'melon', which is thought to help dolphins send out signals.

DOLPHINS ARE REALLY SMALL-TOOTHED WHALES.

THE BOTTLENOSE DOLPHIN IS HIGHLY INTELLIGENT. IT IS OFTEN USED TO PERFORM IN ZOOS.

The bottle-nose dolphin has a curved mouth leading into a lower jaw that projects beyond the upper jaw, giving it its well-known 'smile'. Dolphin skin is sensitive to touch and scars easily.

Like whales, dolphins navigate and communicate using sounds. By forcing air past valves and flaps located just below its blowhole, a dolphin can make at least 32 different sounds, including whistles, clicks, squawks, barks and groans. However, its high frequency clicks do not carry as far underwater as the low frequency noises made by whales.

Many of the sounds are too high for humans to hear so we need instruments that detect and register them. The whistling language by which they talk has been named 'delphinese' by scientists.

DOLPHINS ARE BORN TAIL FIRST, NOT HEAD FIRST, LIKE MOST MAMMALS.

Navigation System

A dolphin navigates by making clicking sounds, which bounce off objects ahead and are echoed back. Many dolphins get trapped and die in fishing nets because the holes in the net don't offer a surface for the echo to bounce off and the dolphins think there is no obstacle ahead.

OPERATION SUNFLOWER

In 1974, Dr. Horace Dobbs swam in the sea with a wild dolphin. That encounter changed his life and the lives of many others, for Dr. Dobbs founded the International Dolphin Watch, an organisation that studies wild dolphins. In the late 1980s, Dr. Dobbs took Bill, a man ill with depression since 1974, to meet Simo, a wild dolphin off the Welsh coast. After swimming with Simo, Bill said he felt much love. The next day, after years of not wanting to go outside, Bill rushed out of the hotel down to the harbour to meet the dolphin. In the wake of this, 'Operation Sunflower' was set up, in which severely depressed people are taken to spend time with wild dolphins.

Dolphins swim fast and feed by making shallow dives. They surface several times a minute.

Hermit Crabs

Hermit crabs live in empty mollusc shells. Often they take in a lodger – a sea anemone. The anemone attaches itself to the top of the shell and acts as a bodyguard, using its stinging tentacles to scare off predators. When the crab moves to a larger shell, it taps the anemone as a warning and moves it to the new home.

Heike

In AD 12, two Japanese noble families, the Heike and the Genji, fought for years to rule Japan. The tyrannical Heike were finally defeated in the naval battle of Dannoura in the straits of Shimonoseki and in disgrace threw themselves into the sea where they were transformed into crabs. Since then crabs are supposed to have Heike features on their shells.

Crustacean Symbols

To Buddhists, the crab symbolises the sleep of death. In Africa it is the symbol of evil. In the East, a lobster is a good omen and is often shown without claws. In ancient Greece it was considered sacred and in China was a sign of wealth and a happy marriage.

Route March

In Jamaica, land crabs live in rock crevices. Once a year they head for the beaches to breed. Long lines of crabs march purposefully towards the sea, scrambling over anything in their path, even houses.

Crabs

THE ANCIENT GREEK word for crab was 'karkinos' and its Latin name is 'cancer'. Both of these names come from the early Indian word 'crenate', meaning to break or crush. For some reason crabs have always had a bad reputation. The crab's huge pincer claws have probably caused this but in spite of its appearance, the crab is not vicious and will avoid humans if possible.

CRABS VARY IN SIZE greatly, from just 1.25 cm (0.5 in) to the giant crab of Japan, which can span 40 cm (16 in) from claw tip to claw tip.

Sea creatures do not need supporting skeletons like land dwellers because the water itself supports them. Large spider crabs do not come on land because, unsupported by water, they cannot move their long legs. However, water is more difficult or backwards. Most of its joints are like our knee joints and can only bend in one direction.

The type of claws a crab has is a clue to its way of life. Slow-moving crabs that feed on molluscs have strong claws to crack shells. In fact, the claws of a morro crab are so powerful that they can crush a man's hand. Those that rely on catching moving prey have claws with serrated edges.

THE FIDDLER CRAB HAS A HUGE MENACING-LOOKING LEFT CLAW.

to move through than air, so the shapes of sea creatures have evolved to create the least resistance when moving. This is why the crab's body is streamlined and flattened. Most crabs don't swim but walk or run across the ocean bed. A crab can scuttle sideways much faster than it can move forwards

Lobsters

LOBSTERS, LIKE CRABS, HAVE skeletons on the outside of their bodies, enclosing their internal organs in a natural armour, to which the muscles are attached on the inside. Lobsters come in many colours: yellow, grey, greenish-brown, dusty orange, blue and spotted.

THE LOBSTER was made inside out and upside-down. Not only does it carry its skeleton on the outside of the body, most of the nervous system is along its belly instead of its back and its kidneys are behind its forehead. A lobster's brain, which is around the size of a

A LOBSTER'S TEETH ARE IN ITS STOMACH.

pinhead, is in two parts – one above and one below its throat. It listens with its legs, through tiny sensory hairs that pick up underwater vibrations, and tastes with its antennae and leg-like mouthparts.

Lobsters grow by shedding (moulting) and replacing their shells 25 to 30 times in the first seven years of life. When moulting, the lobster hides in a rocky crevice and waits, eating nothing. Gradually its body and muscles become flabby and powerless. The shell splits and the defenceless lobster struggles out. Now extremely soft and vulnerable, its body absorbs water until after a few hours it is much larger. The new shell hardens rapidly and after three days the lobster is ready to leave its hideaway.

Lost Legs

Would you notice if an arm or leg fell off? Probably! A lobster can lose a walking leg, a claw or an antennae and carry on as if nothing has happened. In fact, it can discard one deliberately to escape a predator and later grow it back. Biologists say this indicates a primitive nervous system and less sensitivity to pain than humans or many other species.

Lobsters' Trail

Lobsters tend to stay in one place but each autumn lobsters in the Bahamas move from reefs to deeper water. To cross open areas they form a long column of 50 or more. Each lobster hooks its front legs around the tail of the lobster in front and then they go across the seabed faster than a person can swim. One tagged column travelled a record distance of 362 km (225 miles).

Lobsters and crabs are scavengers. They eat all kinds of rubbish and left-overs from the seabed. They also eat fish and starfish.

Toothy Grin

A crocodile may have around 40 teeth set in the sockets of its large jawbones. When closed, the jaws interlock, giving the crocodile a powerful grip on its prey. As soon as the sharp points of a crocodile's teeth wear down, the teeth are replaced by new ones growing behind. When the Nile crocodile has finished a meal, it takes a nap with its mouth open. This is the cue for a little bird called the spur-winged plover to hop inside and clean the crocodile's dirty teeth.

Crocodile Test

In days of old, one Arabian test of innocence was called the 'Ordeal by Crocodile'. During an 'Ordeal by Crocodile', accused people were thrown into a pit of crocodiles. If the accused came out unharmed, they were innocent. If not, they were guilty. Needless to say, most people were found guilty! In west Africa, just to be attacked by a crocodile was a sign of guilt. This was because crocodiles were thought to be the souls of murdered people seeking their revenge.

Crocodiles

Crocodile fossils have been found dating back to before 65 million years ago – the same time that dinosaurs walked the Earth. In fact, crocodiles are direct descendants of the prehistoric archosaurs. Crocodiles are clever reptiles; they learn fast and can move with lightning speed.

Despite being smart for a reptile, a crocodile has a very small brain. The crocodile uses stealth and strength to catch and overpower its prey. Lying still in the water, it often looks as harmless as a floating log. Then, when a deer or small mammal comes to the riverbank to drink, with a mighty sweep of its tail, the crocodile knocks the creature down, seizes it and holds it underwater until it drowns. One third of a crocodile's weight is in its tail.

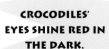

CROCODILES' EYES SHINE RED IN THE DARK.

A crocodile will attack anything that goes near the water. It is an opportunist, seizing any animal that passes its way – so dangling arms and legs are in danger of being grabbed.

A crocodile can crash its long jaws shut with a force strong enough to crush the bones of a small animal. However, once closed, the jaw muscles are so weak in opening that a human can hold its mouth shut with one hand.

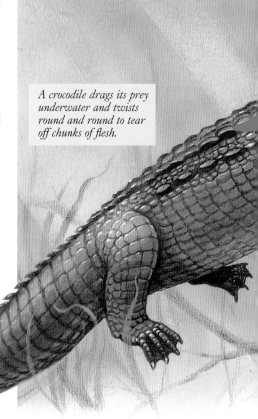

A crocodile drags its prey underwater and twists round and round to tear off chunks of flesh.

LIKE ALL REPTILES, CROCODILES ARE COLD-BLOODED.

Intimidating as its teeth are, they are geared for clamping, not chewing. Nile crocodiles work together to catch food, forming a dam with their bodies to trap fish. With larger prey, one crocodile holds it down while the other rips it apart.

A crocodile is nature's submarine. The crocodile has a system of valves, which automatically close when it dives to protect its ears, nose and throat from water. The eyes sit on top of the head and stay above water when the rest of the body is submerged. A crocodile can stay underwater for as long as an hour. When swimming underwater, thousands of tiny crystals embedded in a crocodile's eyes collect light and allow it amazing underwater vision. A crocodile does not use its feet as paddles to swim, but swings its tail from side to side to push back the water and propel itself along at high speed.

The average crocodile can have around 4.5-7 kg (10-15 lb) of stones in its stomach at any one time. A crocodile swallows stones to add the weight needed to stay underwater, and also to help grind up its food.

American alligators live in swamps. In the dry season, when the swamps dry up, they live in holes in the ground which stay damp.

Crocs and Alligators

A crocodile has a larger snout than an alligator and when its jaws are shut, the fourth tooth on each side of its lower jaw sticks out. An alligator has no teeth showing. The word 'alligator' comes from the Spanish for lizard 'el largato.' Try saying this fast a few times and it sounds like 'alligator'. An alligator is smaller than a crocodile and is found only in the Americas.

CROCODILE TEARS

It was thought long ago that a crocodile moaned and sighed like a person in distress in order to lure its prey. Whatever or whoever came to investigate the pitiful sound was snatched and devoured. One Indian belief is that a crocodile begins to eat the body of its victim, hangs over its prey, then 'sheds tears' before finishing the meal. This is probably where the term 'crocodile tears' comes from. In truth, a crocodile only eats what it can swallow whole, so it often drags its prey to an underwater lair and leaves the body to rot until it is soft enough to swallow.

Water-holding Frog

On the rare occasion when rain comes to the deserts of central Australia, the water-holding frog shoots out from its underground home and, using loose skin to form bags, collects more than half its own weight in water. As the next rainfall in the desert may not be for five or six years, the frog stores this water by oozing a membrane-like envelope around itself to seal in the water.

Frog Parliament

The croaking of a group of frogs is often called a 'frog parliament', meaning a lot of noise, without much being achieved! Long ago, the frog parliament asked the Greek god Zeus to give it a king. A king was provided and the first thing he did was throw a log into the frog's pool. The log landed with a splash and impressed the frogs but, after a while, the king became lazy. The frogs grew tired of a king who did nothing and asked for another. This time Zeus sent a stork, which gobbled them all up!

Frogs use their powerful back legs to leap from lily pad to lily pad looking for flies to eat.

Frogs and toads

FROGS AND TOADS belong to a group of animals called amphibians. This means they are able to live both in water and on land. Hundreds of years ago, these small creatures were thought to be lucky and to kill one was believed to bring bad luck. Perhaps this is because neither frogs nor toads are likely to be far from fresh water and, as water is so precious, the sight of a frog or toad was a good sign.

IN ANCIENT EGYPT, FROGS were used as symbols of new life and resurrection. This may be because a frog changes form very dramatically during the early stage of its life. From one of a jelly-like mass of eggs, it grows into a tadpole – a round, black body with gills on either side of its neck, a tail and no legs.

Gradually the tail shrinks away to nothing and legs start to grow.

Amazing though this is, a greater change now takes place. The oxygen-absorbing gills gradually disappear and lungs grow inside the body instead.

Frogs live both on land and in water, and have a delicate porous skin through which the frog takes in oxygen. Its absorbent skin makes it vulnerable to the effects of fertilisers, pesticides and chemical pollutants in water and rain and by changes in the ozone layer, which allow more ultraviolet radiation

THERE ARE OVER 2,500 SPECIES OF FROG AND TOAD.

through to the planet. This can cause mutations (genetic changes) resulting in some frogs being born with missing eyes, missing or deformed limbs and, in some cases, extra pairs of legs.

A FROG'S SKIN IS ALWAYS MOIST, EVEN IN DRY WEATHER.

Frogs and toads are gardeners' friends as they eat many of the creatures that damage garden plants. Their diets are slightly different, so they can survive happily on the same patch of ground. Both eat beetles, flies and woodlice but a toad will gobble up ants, while a frog prefers slugs and snails.

When a tasty insect comes into sight, the frog flips the back of its tongue over and forward, shooting it out of its mouth with speed to grab its meal.

A frog's skin is not actually slimy but it is always moist, even in dry weather, because it contains special glands, which produce secretions to keep it moist, smooth and supple. Toads have a tougher, drier, warty skin.

SOME FROGS AND TOADS ARE POISONOUS.

This means they are unable to 'breathe' through their skins as frogs do but they survive better on land in dry places.

The common toad hides during the daytime, emerging only at dusk to feed on flies and other insects.

Strange Weather

Throughout history, there have been strange reports of it 'raining' frogs and toads. On 24 September 1973, The Times newspaper reported that the day before, tens of thousands of small toads rained from the sky on to the French village of Brignoles. In a letter dated 24 October 1683, John Collinges, a Quaker scholar, tells of toads raining on Acle, UK, and running into the houses in the village. In AD 4, the Roman writer, Pliny wrote of a shower of frogs that blocked Greek roads for days.

PRESERVED ALIVE

Frogs and toads seem to have an almost miraculous ability to survive for huge lengths of time holed up in tiny spaces. In 1719, the French Academy of Sciences reported that a toad, 'middle-sized but lean and filling up the whole vacant space' was found in a cavity inside the trunk of an elm tree. In 1851, a frog, found alive inside a piece of coal, was shown at the Great Exhibition, London, UK, and in 1865, the Leeds Mercury, a newspaper from the UK, reported that a live toad had been found in a 200 million year old block of limestone quarried at Hartlepool Waterworks, UK. It is not known how the animal found its way into the block.

Icy Duck

Ducks have been seen helping each other when injured and in trouble. Once a duck was spotted with its feet frozen into the ice of a frozen pond. It was quacking in distress but, before any onlookers could help, a group of ducks rushed up and began fussing around the trapped duck's feet. Eventually, the extra heat caused by the ducks walking on the ice melted it and the duck was set free.

Father Goose

The parents of some ducklings living on a city lake were killed, but luckily the ducklings were adopted by a gander (male goose). Each day, the gander led the ducklings to a nearby house where bread was put out for them. It then stood by while the ducklings ate. When the ducklings were full, the gander ate what they had left and shepherded them back to the lake.

When ducks dive underwater for food, they tip forward, stretching their necks, leaving just their tail feathers poking above the water.

Ducks and geese

TOGETHER WITH SWANS, ducks and geese belong to the same family of waterfowl. They live on land and in water. Ducks differ from geese in that they have squatter bodies and shorter necks and legs, but neither ducks nor geese have legs well-suited to walking on land. Their legs are set very far back, which gives them their characteristic waddle.

WHEN IN WATER, ducks and geese balance like rowing boats, using their broad, webbed feet as paddles to row themselves along. On the surface of the water they look as if they are moving without effort but underneath they are paddling furiously.

If you have ever seen a flock of migrating geese winging across the sky, a similar thing is happening in the sky. Behind the beauty of the

GANDERS ARE BELIEVED TO 'TALK' TO GOSLINGS WHILE THEY ARE STILL IN THE EGG.

Geese migrate to winter feeding-grounds each year after the breeding season.

V-formation is a lot of hard work, especially for the lead goose. It controls the speed of the flock, its direction and its height from the ground. It is also the chief lookout and spots any danger ahead. Migrating geese and ducks fly in a V-formation because the air rushing past the leader gives an extra lift to others. Every bird in the group takes a turn at being leader.

When a gosling (baby goose) hatches, the first animal or thing it sees becomes imprinted in its memory. It regards the animal as its kin and follows it everywhere. Viennese zoologist Korad Lorenz found that his goslings adopted many things as their mothers, including a ball, a block of wood and an Alsatian dog.

Swans

SWANS HAVE BEEN seen through the ages as symbols of purity, grace and beauty, as well as loyalty, nobility and courage. With their snowy white, curly feathers, long gracefully arched necks and elegant wingspans, swans are truly graceful and beautiful birds. Riding high on the surface of a lake or river, swans glide serenely by, looking as if nothing in the world could trouble them.

Swan Upping

In England, swans on open and common water belong to either the Crown (the king or the queen) or trade guilds. At one time, they all belonged to the Crown but during the 15th century some of the swans on the River Thames were given to the trade guilds. Since then, all the swans that belong to the guilds are marked with a nick in the beak, while the Crown's swans are left unmarked.

Swan Song

A long-held belief is that swans sing just once before they die. Silent all their lives, their death song is said to be so haunting it would break the heart of the listener. Out of this, the phrase 'swan song' has developed and means a person's last act.

Swans learn to fly at just three months old when they make their long migration south.

FLOCKS OF SWANS consist of separate families, each with an adult pair plus their fledglings (offspring). Baby swans are called cygnets and, when born, they are not white like their parents but a dingy grey colour. It takes some time for them to turn into recognisable swans. A female swan is called a pen and a male swan, a cob. The loyalty and faithfulness of swans is both legendary and real – they mate with the same partner for the whole of their lives.

SWANS CAN FLY AT SPEEDS OF UP TO 80 KM/H (50 MPH).

smaller birds to tease. Little grebes have been seen tweaking swans' tails and then diving beneath the water out of harm's reach. Once the swans have turned away, the grebes bob back up again to repeat the joke.

WHEN SWANS ARE ALARMED THEY STRETCH THEIR NECKS UPWARD.

Swans can get angry if anything or anyone moves on to their territory. A sweep of a swan's wing is strong enough to break a human arm and its beak can deliver quite a peck. Swans show tremendous courage when protecting their young and will attack anything they see as a threat. Swans are very regal and dignified and this makes them a tempting target for the

Penguins

Penguins are seen as comedians of the bird world, clowns in their movements and behaviour. Standing side by side in large groups, perfectly still and upright, they can look like well-drilled soldiers waiting for a command. Although they are birds, penguins cannot fly and use their wings to swim with great speed underwater. Their short legs with webbed feet act as rudders.

Penguin Adventure

A penguin was found asleep on the doorstep of a house by Wellington Harbour, North Island, New Zealand. It was a Fiordland penguin, usually found off the coast of South Island. Two attempts were made to release it on a beach 84 km (52 miles) away. The first time it climbed into the travelling cage and went to sleep, the second time it swam away but reappeared on the Wellington Harbour doorstep 24 hours later. Finally, the penguin was flown south in style and released into its home waters.

Emperor penguins are the largest penguin species. Adults can measure nearly 1.2 metres (4 ft) tall and weigh up to 41 kg (90 lb).

Penguins spend much of their time underwater, coming ashore only to breed and moult. Their feathers are short and glossy and most importantly, waterproof.

Emperor penguins, the largest of all the penguins, never actually come to land but gather on the pack ice of the Antarctic seas.

THE RARE GALAPAGOS PENGUIN IS THE ONLY SPECIES TO LIVE NEAR THE EQUATOR.

Once a year, the female penguin lays one egg and then returns to the water while the male incubates the egg on its feet for 64 days.

Adélie penguins show true grit when they make mammoth migration treks across barren ice to their Antarctic rookeries (breeding grounds). They have been known to walk 805 km (500 miles) or more in their slow, awkward waddle. The males watch over the eggs until they hatch, then they walk another 157-257 km (97-160 miles) to the sea to feed.

Pelicans

FOOD-CATCHING features strongly in the lives of pelicans. They are large, strong birds that feed on fish, which they catch when swimming in shallow water or by diving from the air. The skin under the lower bills extends into a pouch with which they trawl for fish. Food so dominates the lives of pelicans and their appetites are so huge, that they will even take fish from a human hand.

The Pelican's Beak

Many years ago on the islands of Fiji, lived a fisherman named Ratu Tatanga who wove the largest fish traps around. The pelican, who at that time could only catch one fish at a time in its thin beak, told Ratu of its plight. As a reward Ratu gave the pelican one of his fish traps to use as a beak so that the pelican could catch as many fish as possible in one scoop.

THE GREAT WHITE pelican is well adapted for aquatic life. Its short, strong legs propel it in the water and help its rather ungainly take off from the water's surface. Once up in the air, the long-winged pelican is a powerful flier and often travels with other pelicans in a spectacular V-formation group.

PELICANS EITHER LIVE NEAR THE COAST OR ON INLAND LAKES AND MARSHES.

A pelican's pouch is simply a scoop. As it pushes its bill underwater, the pouch fills up with water and fish. On lifting its head, the pouch contracts, forcing out the water and leaving just the fish.

Large numbers of pelicans breed together in colonies. The females lay two to four eggs in a nest of sticks and the young are cared for by both parents. A mother pelican, returning from a trip to the sea, regurgitates half-digested fish into her beak pouch and the young dip at the food. They often tumble in headfirst, legs kicking in the air as they scrape for the bits at the bottom.

Brown pelicans are the smallest of all the pelicans and hunt differently from the rest. They catch fish by diving at top speed into the water from 15 m (50 ft) high. When they dive, they hold their wings back and curve their necks into S-shapes. Their necks have cushioning airsacs to take some of the impact of the plunge into the water.

Pelicans love a good feed, but sometimes they don't know when to stop! One couple out fishing were joined by a hopeful pelican. They decided to feed it, having no idea of the huge quantities pelicans can eat. The bird ate without pausing until, in the end, it was so full it fell over!

A pelican's most dramatic and distinguishing feature is its huge pouch that hangs beneath its long, broad bill.

Pelican and Christ

In medieval times, it was thought that as young pelicans grew, they often rebelled against the adult male bird and provoked its anger, so that it killed them. When the mother pelican returned to the nest, she pierced her own breast with her beak and revived the young with her blood. Another belief was that the mother pelican fed them with its own blood. Christians linked this legend to Christ and the sacrifice he made for humankind. This is probably why many churches have pelicans in stained glass windows or carved on lecterns.

Seals

The Selkie

The Selkie are the mythical seal folk of the Orkney and Shetland Islands, UK. On land they appear in human form but, to travel through the sea, they wear sealskins.

A Selkie woman can be captured by the theft of her sealskin. The clan MacCodum of North Uist, in the Outer Hebrides, Scotland, are known as 'Silochd nan Ron', which translates as 'the Offspring of the Seals'.

The common seal has been known to make dives that last up to 30 minutes.

W ITH THEIR LARGE, dreamy eyes, supple grace in water and ability to look almost like a different animal on land, seals have long been linked with magical powers. On land they have to drag themselves forwards with their flippers but in water they are highly skilful swimmers and divers and can stay in water for very long periods, diving to great depths.

A SEAL'S BODY IS TORPEDO SHAPED WITH THICK LAYERS OF BLUBBER UNDER ITS SKIN.

Seal Sanctuary

Rescued, orphaned and injured seals often have to be taught to feed themselves, which is vital for them to survive in the wild. Large, an injured grey seal taken in by the Orkney Seal Rescue Centre, UK, only ate fish when it thought no-one was watching. When humans were around it would only be hand-fed – probably hoping it could stay and eat free food in the sanctuary for a little bit longer!

IF YOU TRY SWIMMING underwater with your mouth open, you soon end up spluttering and swallowing water. A seal can close its nostrils while diving and strong muscles prevent water entering its throat when it opens its mouth underwater to feed.

The flow of blood to heart muscle and brain is automatically slowed. This reduces oxygen use

THE WORD 'SEAL' COMES FROM THE ANGLO-SAXON 'SEOLB' MEANING 'TO DRAG'.

and allows the seal to stay underwater for longer.

Weddell seals make deeper, longer dives than any other seals. They can hold their breath for 30 minutes and dive to depths of 457 m (1,500 ft) where the pressure would crush the hull of some boats.

The pups of bearded seals are born on the drifting ice floes of the Arctic and take to the sea almost at once. At less than a week old they can dive to 250 m (820 ft) and stay underwater for a period of five minutes.

Hippopotamuses

THE THIRD LARGEST LAND animals, found only in Africa, hippopotamuses were named by the ancient Greeks ('hippos' meaning 'horse' and 'potamos' meaning 'river') who thought that their cries sounded similar to the neighing of horses. Large and bulky, hippopotamuses are generally timid but can be aggressive if disturbed. They are well adapted to spend much of their lives in water.

Rerat

The hippopotamus was an important figure in ancient Egypt. The goddess Rerat, one of the keepers of the gates passed by the soul on its journey after death, was shown as a hippopotamus standing on hind legs. The goddess was a symbol of fertility, often shown pregnant and standing upright.

Rescue Attempt

A hippopotamus' amazing attempt to save a deer was caught on film, showing its bravery and defensiveness. The hippopotamus beat off a crocodile that was savaging a deer and made several attempts to lift the deer with its head. Finally it put its huge mouth over the deer's mouth in an attempt to resuscitate the poor animal. For all the hippopotamus' efforts, the deer died and the hippopotamus howled in anguish.

WHEN HIPPOPOTAMUSES are in water they lie with much of their vast bodies submerged, often with only their eyes, ears and noses poking above the surface. They are able to close their nostrils when underwater and secrete an oily substance which protects their bodies. They swim and dive well and can walk on the bottom of a river or lake. When on land, they eat short grass and plants and can reach speeds of up to 32 km/h (20 mph).

Baby hippopotamuses can swim within five minutes of being born but to escape crocodiles and their not-too-gentle fathers, young hippopotamuses spend much time on their mothers' backs.

THE PYGMY HIPPOPOTAMUS IS APPROXIMATELY HALF THE SIZE OF THE HIPPOPOTAMUS.

Hippopotamuses have a social etiquette about who stands where in the river. The female and the young stay in the centre, while the males, each in his own patch, range along the edges. If a male wanders into a female's territory, he must lower himself into the water if she stands up. If he fails,

THE PYGMY HIPPOPOTAMUS IS EXTREMELY RARE AND IS EVEN EXTINCT IN SOME AREAS.

he will most likely be set upon by all the other females around. Male hippos sometimes bully younger hippopotamuses so this may be why females insist the males submerge themselves where they can do no harm.

The pygmy hippopotamus, as well as being much smaller then its giant relative, is much less aquatic. It lives near water but stays on land for most of the time, feeding at night on leaves, swamp vegetation and fallen fruit.

Hippopotamuses live in groups of up to 15 or so, led by an old male.

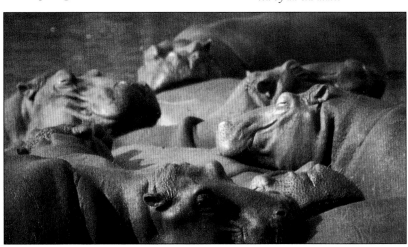

Ice Holes

Polar bears love to eat seals. A bear lies in wait by the blow holes seals make in the ice, and then when a seal pops its head up to breathe some air, the bear grabs it. Sometimes a bear will block up other breathing holes in the area to force the seals to use one particular blow hole and so increase its chances of catching a meal. One polar bear was even seen to throw handfuls of ice at a seal it missed!

Arctic Ancestors

One legend from the people of Lapland says that polar bears were thought to be ancestors of the Lapps, who called the bear grandfather.

To the peoples of the northern lands, the polar bear was king of the beasts – swift, deadly, supremely powerful and a killer of men. This may be because the Arctic peoples wear sealskins, rub seal oil on their bodies and eat seal meat, and the polar bear, which likes seal meat, gets confused.

Little Bears

When born in November or December, polar bear cubs are around the size of a rat. They first see daylight in March or April and are then the size of a cat. The phrase 'licked into shape' comes from the ancient belief that bear cubs were born as shapeless balls of fur and the mother bear shaped them into baby bears with her tongue.

Polar bears

THE LONE WHITE HUNTER, found only in the Arctic, the polar bear wanders the white wastes of its icy world, king of this windswept and hostile environment. Equally at home on icy land and in water, always on the move and almost invisible with its white fur against the white landscape, the polar bear inspires both awe at its beauty and fear of its power.

THE POLAR BEAR is nature's perfect stealth weapon. Almost invisible to the naked eye by day, it is truly invisible to modern night-vision glasses and even infrared cameras.

A polar bear's fur is unique. It is a mass of hollow hairs, each with a smooth surface and a rough-coated core, which work like fibre-optics, with light entering each hair at its open end and bouncing down the hair tube until it reaches the bear's black skin at its root.

Polar bears have hairs on the soles of their feet to stop them slipping on the ice. When a polar bear gets too hot, it jumps into the sea to cool down.

POLAR BEARS ARE CONSTANTLY ON THE MOVE, TRAVELLING UP TO 120 KM (75 MILES) A WEEK.

Black absorbs more light and heat than other colours – perfect for a bear in a cold climate. Added to that, the hairs also let light in all the way round. These hairs also take in ultra-violet light and convert it to infrared light to heat the bear's body.

While the bear's hair is trapping warm light, it is also scattering light, giving the hair its whiteness. But that's not all the hairs can do! Running down the centre of each is a central core of membranes that gives the hair strength without weight, so although the bear's coat is thick and warm, it is not too heavy. Added to that, in among the hairs are air pockets, a built-in life jacket that helps the bear float in the Arctic seas.

POLAR BEARS ARE THE LARGEST FLESH-EATERS ON LAND.

Polar bears are one of the seven species of true bear, and the only one to inhabit the Arctic regions.

A Warm Threat

Polar bears may be threatened by global warming. Probably due to global warming, Arctic ice sheets have shrunk northwards in recent years. Seals, the polar bear's favourite food, live and rear their young on the edge of these ice sheets. As their homes move northwards, this takes the seals away from the rich waters where they normally find fish and krill on which to feed. If the seal numbers drop, then polar bears might struggle to survive.

CURIOUS CREATURES

Polar bears can be very curious and persistent in their interest. In 1969, a polar bear travelling on top of an ice floe drifted alongside a coastguard vessel in the Canadian Arctic. The crew fed it black molasses, jam, salami sandwiches, a jar of peanut butter, some salt pork, lots of chocolate bars and an apple, which it spat out in disgust. When the food ran out, the bear climbed on board the ship. Not sure what to expect from a wild polar bear, the crew turned the water hoses on it. Big mistake! The polar bear loved that even more than the food and even held its arms up for the crew to hose underneath!

Strong Swimmers

An excellent swimmer, the polar bear jumps into the water like a dog or slides in backwards. It can stay underwater for two minutes at a time. Using only its front legs, it cruises at about 10 km/h (6 mph). Polar bears have been seen 80 km (49 miles) from land or ice floes. One was spotted swimming as far away as 322 km (200 miles) north of Greenland.

Floating Beds

Just under the ocean surface, kelp leaves spread out like a mattress while, deep below, the roots are anchored in sand and rocks. When sea otters prepare for bed, they grab floating ends of sea kelp and roll over and over, wrapping themselves in the strands. The otters sleep safely, pups in their mothers' arms, while the kelp keeps them from drifting away during the night.

Even adult otters are playful. They enjoy sliding down muddy banks and rushing about.

Otters

SMALL ANIMALS with big hearts, otters are wild animals that live happily alongside humans. Within their family groups they are very affectionate and loyal creatures with a natural curiosity about the world around them. Otters love to play on the riverbanks and take great delight in exploring and trying something new.

Otters live mainly along the rivers and seacoasts. In both environments, fish and eels are their main source of food.

The river otter has a long, slender body, covered in brown fur, which is paler on its front and belly, small ears, a long thick tail and webbed feet. Its large, black feet act as flippers. The river otter averages 90-120 cm (35-47 in) in length and has a tail 40 cm

BABY OTTERS HAVE TO BE TAUGHT HOW TO SWIM BY THEIR PARENTS.

(15 in) long. River otters live in a holt or den in the riverbank and are most active at night. They need clean rivers with a good fish supply and each otter may well range over 10 km (6 miles).

The sea otter is around 1 m (39 in) in length with a tail 25-37 cm (10-15 in) long and dense, dark brown, silky fur which traps an insulating layer of air to keep the animal warm.

Beavers

BEAVERS ARE SOCIABLE, peaceful, hardworking and faithful. They live in close-knit families and are master homebuilders. Beavers lead semi-aquatic lives and are excellent swimmers. They are always found near waterways surrounded by dense woodland and feed on the bark and twigs from trees. They also use the wood to build their amazingly complex dams and lodges.

Timber!

A beaver is a small creature, standing about 50 cm (2 ft) high on its hind legs, yet it can bring down a tall tree using only its teeth. It chews around the tree trunk until most of the tree is balanced on a fine point off-centre. It then waits for the tree to fall.

BEFORE THEY START to raise a family, male and female beavers find a stream and create their own pond by felling trees with their sharp teeth. Their dams are made of logs, piled up horizontally from the riverbed and held down and sandwiched together with layers of mud and stones. It is not unusual for a dam to be 100 m (330 ft) long, 5 m (16 ft) wide at the bottom, 1.5 m (5 ft) wide at the top and 3.5 m (12 ft) high.

Once the dam is in place, beavers build their home, or lodge. This is built rather like an Indian teepee, with one or two underwater entrances, an internal platform just above the water level and a roof of heavily woven thatch plastered with mud, which sets firm and keeps out intruders.

IF A BEAVER LOSES A TOOTH, IT WILL USUALLY DIE.

BEAVERS HAVE WEBBED FEET AND FLAT TAILS, WHICH THEY USE AS RUDDERS WHEN SWIMMING.

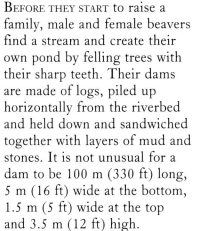

It takes a pair of beavers about six months to build a lodge if they are taking their time but, if rushed, they can do it in a month.

From their pond, the beavers then build a network of small canals to reach the trees on which the whole family feeds. Branches are then ferried back to the lodge and stuck upright in the mud at the bottom of the pond. By winter, the lodge is quite well-stocked.

Beavers are well adapted for their aquatic habits. Their dense fur provides both waterproofing and insulation and their ears and nostrils can be closed off, allowing them to stay underwater for up to 15 minutes at a time.

A beaver's favourite foods are aspen and poplar bark. Its teeth keep growing until it dies, so a beaver must keep chewing to wear them down.

The Beaver's Tail

Long ago, fire spread across the forest in which all the animals lived. The beaver called the river folk together and they built a dam to flood the path of the fire. All the animals jumped for safety into the water but a burning tree fell across the beaver's beautiful, bushy tail. Luckily the beaver was pulled to safety, but its lovely tail was flattened and burned and has been hairless ever since.

Myth

LONG AGO, BEFORE we had films, computers, televisions and books, people gathered around fires and told each other stories. Some tales were attempts to explain things people didn't understand, such as traits and characteristics they saw in the animals around them. Bigger myths explained how life and the world were created, why the seasons change and how humankind first appeared on Earth. These myths often contained animals, because animals were very much part of life. So animals became symbols that helped us understand our world.

MANY MYTHOLOGICAL ANIMALS ARE BASED ON REAL ANIMALS WITH HUMAN EXAGGERATIONS.

MANY PEOPLE USED TO BELIEVE THAT MYTHICAL CREATURES REALLY EXISTED.

MYTHS ABOUT ANIMALS GROW FROM OUR NEED TO UNDERSTAND THE MYSTERY OF THEIR EXISTENCE.

Garuda

Garuda is one of the oldest mythical birds. It had a human body with an eagle's head, wings and feet and was the divine bird of India. It was called the 'bird of life'. Garuda was the enemy of all serpents that were thought to be evil and made sure it ate a snake every day. It was so large that, when flying, it blotted out the sun. Garuda's face was white, its body golden and its wings scarlet.

The Roc

In Arab and Persian folklore, the roc was such a huge bird, it could carry an elephant in its talons. No one has ever properly described the roc, as it was so large it was impossible to see all of it at any one time. However, the roc was supposed to have two horns on its head and four humps on its back.

Harpy

Harpies were foul-smelling, monstrous creatures with the heads of old women on the bodies of birds. Their feathers could not be damaged and they flew with the speed of the wind. The name harpy means 'snatcher' and the ancient Greeks thought that harpies were spirits of the wind who snatched up those mortals that the gods wished to see disappear and carried them to the Underworld.

Mythical birds

BIRDS DO ONE OF THE things humans cannot – they fly. In ancient times, the sky was the source of much that was unknown and uncontrollable – lightning, rain, wind, hail and snow. Birds, which flew and survived in that environment, were seen as creatures with superior powers, messengers of the gods or even gods themselves.

ONE OF THE most magical of birds was the phoenix, a mystical bird which lived alone for 500 years. It then sang its final song before burning itself in a specially built nest, set alight by the sun's rays. From the ashes of the burned phoenix came a worm, which grew into another phoenix.

Because the phoenix was immortal and never died, it was thought that there was always a phoenix somewhere in the world, although only one at a time.

Huge birds are part of Native American mythology, especially the thunderbird.

Many years ago, when the world was young, two Passamaquoddy Indians set out to find where thunder came from. They journeyed to two high mountains, which were constantly moving together and then apart. The first warrior leapt through the gap but the second one was caught and squashed.

THE HO-OO IS THE JAPANESE PHOENIX. THE HO IS THE MALE AND THE OO IS FEMALE.

The phoenix was a mythical bird, said to live in a sacred wood in paradise.

The first one continued and saw a camp of wigwams on the plain below him. Men with wings came out of the wigwams and flew away over the mountains. This was the home of the thunderbirds.

The Ziz was a huge, ancient bird that ruled all other birds. With its massive wings, the Ziz protected smaller birds from harm and the Earth from the storms that blew from the south. Its eggs were so big that when one accidentally fell to the Earth, its contents flooded six cities.

Thunderbird

Storms were supposedly caused when the thunderbird broke through the clouds, clapping its huge wings. Once a Comanche warrior shot a huge bird. As it crashed to the ground, the warrior feared he had shot down the thunderbird. Suddenly a storm brewed up and the hunter was killed by a bolt of lightning.

Caladmus

Caladmus was a supernatural bird that appeared in the Middle Ages. It turned up at the bedside of the seriously ill and perched on the end of the bed. If Caladmus looked at the patients they would recover, but if it looked away from them, they would die.

BIG BIRD

Marlon Lowe was just 10 years old when his red hair turned white. Playing in his garden in Illinois, USA, one day in July 1977, Marlon was snatched from the ground by a huge, black bird with a white ring on its neck. The bird rose into the air, the screaming boy dangling from its talons. Written accounts logged the bird as at least 1.3m (4.5 ft) tall with a hooked bill 45 cm (8 in) long. Fortunately for Marlon, his mother was nearby. She rushed at the bird, screaming and yelling so loudly that the bird dropped her son and flew off. It is rumoured that the very next day, Marlon's hair turned pure white.

Famous Dragon

Legend has it that on Dragon's Hill in Berkshire, England, a brave knight killed a fire-breathing dragon to save a maiden from being the dragon's next sacrificial victim. To this day, there is still a bare patch on Dragon's Hill, where it is said nothing will grow because the dragon's blood was spilled there. The knight became Saint George, patron saint of England.

Constellation

In Greek mythology, the hundred-headed dragon, Draco, guarded the magical garden of the golden apples of Hesperides. The hero of the tale, Hercules, was set the task of stealing the apples from the dragon's orchard. Hercules threw his spear at Draco, killing him immediately. As reward for his previous services, Juno, one of the Greek gods, placed Draco in the heavens where he is now a constellation.

Dragon Ships

In the early days of sea travel, figureheads were carved on ships to give protection to the crew and 'eyes' for the ship to find its way across the seas. Many different animals were used but in northern Europe, dragons or serpents were preferred. The Vikings were famous for their dragon-headed warships or 'Serpents of the Sea'.

Dragons

Say the word 'dragon' and immediately people have a mental picture of what they think one looks like. Eastern or western, all dragons are magical creatures that have a knowledge of the ancient lore of the land. Dragons are thought to be wise and patient but are also creatures whose ferocity is legendary.

In her book, 'Tehuna', Ursula le Guin describes how the great dragon Kalessin, a powerful and ancient creature who lives beyond the rim of the world, comes to the aid of two humans. As Kalessin approaches, the humans stand on a cliff top. They tell of the roar of fire that passes over them, the rattle of the scaly armour, the hiss of the wind on its wings and finally, the clash of talons as it lands on the rock. A dragon does not arrive quietly!

Western legends often show the dragon as a monster that needs to be killed to restore good. Sometimes, western dragons are said to hoard huge piles of treasure or terrorise whole villages full of people.

THE FIRST MAP-MAKERS WROTE 'HERE THERE BE DRAGONS' ON UNEXPLORED LANDS.

Dragons of western myth and legend take all forms, from serpents with wings, to huge reptilian monsters with scaly bodies, wings that could lift a small coach from the ground, and fiery breath.

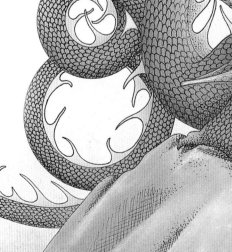

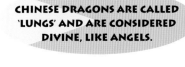

CHINESE DRAGONS ARE CALLED 'LUNGS' AND ARE CONSIDERED DIVINE, LIKE ANGELS.

The dragon has been worshipped at some time or another by almost every race in the world.

Dragons from the east are often wingless, more gentle and likely to give humans gifts or bring good luck.

Throughout history, dragons have often been depicted as green, red, gold and black. However, Chinese and other eastern dragons are more colourful and the hues have meanings – yellow for luck, black for destruction and azure for an important birth. Eastern dragons can also change from the size of a tiny caterpillar to the huge expanse of the universe in a second. They speak in delicate, tinkly voices and rest quietly under the sea or underground.

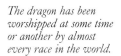

Welsh Flag

For centuries, the red dragon was the national symbol displayed on the war standard of the ancient Britons and the Welsh. The symbol is linked to King Arthur who dreamed that the green Saxon dragon fought the red dragon of the Britons and the red dragon won. Today, the Welsh national flag still features a red dragon.

Dragon Dance

In China, the dragon represents cleverness, good fortune and nobility. The dance of the dragon is used to drive out devils and bring good luck to the community. This dance became popular during the Sung dynasty (AD 960-1279) and today, around 1,000 years later, the colourful dragon dance is still performed at Chinese festivals. At least 12 dancers, one drummer and one leader are needed for the dance. One team performs with a golden dragon 120 m (394 ft) long.

Lion and Unicorn

Since 1603, the British royal arms have been supported by the English lion and the Scottish unicorn. The lion and the unicorn in the following rhyme symbolised the fight between England and Scotland for the throne of England:

The lion and the unicorn
were fighting for the crown.
The lion beat the unicorn
all around the town.
Some gave them white bread and
some gave them brown,
And some gave them plum
cake and drummed
them out of town.

Hippogriff

In Greek mythology, the hippogriff existed in the mountains of Europe. It was a winged horse with an eagle's head and claws. The Moorish hero Rogero escaped from prison on the back of a hippogriff, which his wife, Bradamante, had won from an enchanter.

Magical horses

THERE ARE MANY different types of mythical horses and perhaps because of the sense of freedom horses have, most of them were born from dreams and desires, rather than from fears. This is certainly true of the unicorn which, with its beauty, pure white coat and magical horn, promotes gentleness and selfless love. Pegasus, the winged horse, represents the carrier of dreams and can gallop high above the Earth to the realms of myth and poetry.

THERE HAS BEEN MUCH debate over the centuries as to whether the unicorn was purely mythical or a real beast. If it was real, it has certainly disappeared from

ALEXANDER THE GREAT WAS TAUGHT MANY SKILLS BY THE CENTAUR CHIRON.

The unicorn was believed to become calm in the presence of young maidens.

Earth today. The unicorn was first described by the Greek historian Ctesias in 398 BC. Ctesias was a doctor who worked at the court of the Emperor of Persia, so had probably heard of many interesting sights and tales from travellers. He described the unicorn as having a white body, a dark red head and deep blue eyes, and claimed that it was "exceedingly swift and powerful and no creature, neither the horse or any other, could overtake it."

China's unicorn, the K'I-lin, had a multicoloured body and a horn 3.7 m (12 ft) long. Its voice was said to sound like a thousand wind chimes and it walked so softly its hooves made no sound.

The fierce Muslim unicorn, the Kar-ka-dann, was more like a cow or a bull than a horse. The Kar-ka-dann was so noisy the only thing that could quieten it down was the cooing of a dove.

Only since the Middle Ages has the unicorn become more

THE ADH SIDHE ARE IRISH FAERIE CREATURES WHO APPEAR AS BLACK HORSES.

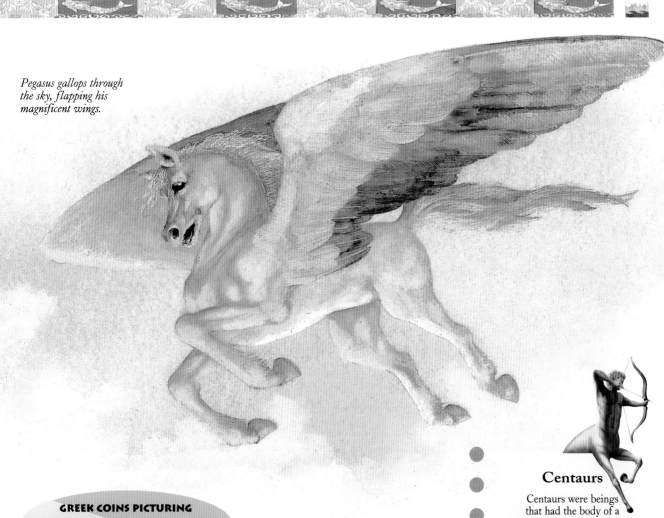

Pegasus gallops through the sky, flapping his magnificent wings.

Centaurs

Centaurs were beings that had the body of a man to the waist and the body and legs of a horse from the waist down. In Greek mythology, centaurs lived in Thessaly but the earliest known tales of them come from Babylon around 2000 BC. The Kassites moved to Babylon in 1750 BC and took with them drawings of centaurs with wings and two tails.

Sleipnir

Sleipnir was an eight-legged horse belonging to Odin, the Norse god of war. Swifter than all horses, no obstacle was too great for Sleipnir, who could gallop across both land and sea. His father was Svadlifari, a giant's horse and his mother was Loki, a Norse god who had changed himself into a mare. Sleipnir once trod on Iceland and the mark of his hoof can be seen today at Asburgi in northeast Iceland.

> **GREEK COINS PICTURING PEGASUS HAVE BEEN FOUND DATING BACK TO AROUND 360 BC.**

horse-like and, in Europe, it is now seen as a white horse with a flowing mane. Although hard to find and gentle by nature, the unicorn was renowned as a fierce fighter. The recommended way to catch a unicorn was to stand in front of a tree with a large trunk and taunt the unicorn until it charged. The hunter would then step aside, exposing the trunk to the unicorn's sharp horn.

The other famous magical horse is Pegasus, the amazing flying horse from Greek mythology. When the Greek hero Perseus killed the snake-haired Gorgon by cutting of her head, blood soaked into the ground. It was from this blood that Pegasus grew. The goddess Minerva tamed him and finally gave him to the Muses who lived on Mount Helicon.

At one time, the Muses held a song contest and the music was so powerful, Mount Helicon started to grow towards heaven. Unhappy about this, the god Poseidon asked Pegasus to strike the mountain with his hoof to make it stop growing. Pegasus struck the rock and the Hippocrene fountain started to flow. From that day, its waters have inspired poets.

> **A UNICORN'S HORN IS CALLED AN ALICORN.**

Mami Wata

Mami Wata is a mermaid water spirit that lives in the waters of western and central Africa. She has long dark hair, hypnotic eyes and very fair skin. It is said she also walks the streets of African towns disguised as a woman.

Mermaid of Zennor

As everyone knows, mermaids are supposed to have beautiful voices and love to sing. In the village of Zennor in Cornwall, UK, there once lived a young man with a voice like a clear, sweet bell. Down in the cove, a mermaid heard his song and fell in love with him. The young man went to live with her under the sea, where they sang beautiful songs together. It is said that in listening to his songs, the fishermen of Zennor knew when it was safe to put to sea and when they should turn for home and a safe harbour.

Triton

In Greek mythology, Triton was the son of the god Poseidon and the sea-goddess Amphitrite. Some tales call him the god of seafarers and say he fathered a whole race of tritons. Nearly all the images of him show him blowing a conch shell. In 1960, the American submarine, the U.S.S. Triton, was the first nuclear-powered submarine to sail around the world completely submerged.

Mermaids

MERMAID LEGENDS are as old as the world's oldest cultures. Always beautiful, usually unhappy, mermaids are women to their waists and below they have a scaly fishtail. A mermaid is often pictured sitting on a rock, looking into a mirror and combing her waist-length golden hair. Records of creatures half human, half fish go back as far as 1800 BC.

TO THE PECH INDIANS of Honduras, USA, the mother of all fish was a nine-eyed mermaid called Sirena. Before a fishing trip they would ask her permission to catch fish, as fishing without her permission was thought to lead to illness or death.

THE JAPANESE MERMAID 'NMGYO' IS A FISH WITH A HUMAN HEAD.

The Principality of Luxembourg, was founded by Count Siegfried, who had a beautiful wife called Melusin. When Siegfried first asked her to marry him she agreed on one

THE POLYNESIAN CREATOR-GOD IS HALF MAN, HALF PORPOISE.

condition, that he would leave her alone for one full day each month. Because he loved her so much, Siegfried agreed. For years, on the first Wednesday of every month, Melusina would go to a network of underground caverns beneath the city and spend the day there. One day, Siegfried followed her and found her as a mermaid, lying in a tub full of water.

The minute she realised her secret had been found out, Melusina jumped from the window into the Alzette River and was never seen again.

There are many tales of mermaids who have fallen in love with a human and chosen a lonely life on land away from their folk. Some tell of human men who have fallen in love with a mermaid and trapped her by taking her 'merskin' while she was dancing on a beach in human form.

Mermaids and mermen are said to be able to turn the sunniest of days into a storm.

Famous Mermaid

The Little Mermaid sits on a rock in the harbour of Copenhagen, Denmark. She was sculpted by Edvard Erikson in 1913 in memory of Hans Christian Anderson who wrote the story of 'The Little Mermaid'. In the story, the mermaid fell in love with a prince and the price she paid to become human and be near him was the loss of her beautiful voice. Sadly, this meant she could never tell him that she loved him.

A FISHING TALE

On 20 April 1814, the Aberdeen Chronicle ran a report that two fishermen returning from Spey Bay, Scotland, were about half a kilometre (quarter of a mile) offshore when they saw a man in the sea with his back to them. The fishermen rowed over to the man and had nearly reached him when he heard them coming and turned. His skin was a brownish colour and his hair grey-green. He had a flat nose, small eyes, a large mouth and very long arms. He was man to the waist but past the waist his body tapered into a fishtail. As the fishermen watched in astonishment, the man dived and resurfaced with a female, who also had a tail.

A Mermaid's Tears

On the Holy Island of Iona, off the coast of Scotland, are grey-green pebbles, said to be the tears of a mermaid who was in love with a saint who lived on the island. The mermaid visited the saint every day but all he would tell her was that to gain a soul she must leave the sea. In despair she knew she could never do this. To this day, all that remains on the shore are the tears she cried.

Kraken

'Kraken' is an old Norse word for a terrifying, many-armed sea creature. Fishermen and sailors told tales of this monster whose back was so long – around 1.6 km (1 mile) – that sometimes it was mistaken for a floating island! Its great tentacles could easily reach the top of a sailing ship's mast or wrap around a boat's hull and drag it to the bottom of the sea.

Kelpie

The kelpie is the water horse of Scottish rivers. Its close relation is the uisage, a water horse found in Scottish and Irish lochs and sea inlets of the UK. Both of these creatures are unfriendly to humans. They look like docile horses but if mounted, they rush off into the water and eat their riders. Once on a water horse, it is impossible to dismount. However, if a human manages to bridle a kelpie, it must obey his or her command.

Reported sightings of the Loch Ness monster go back as far as AD 6.

Water creatures

Most countries have stories of mythical creatures that inhabit the seas, rivers, lakes, wells and pools of the world. Earth's waters are so vast and deep our imaginations have run wild. There have been many sightings of water monsters, but they are still a mystery. Although it is likely they are creatures of myth, built around sightings of swimming otters or large fish, there is always the possibility that some of these monstrous creatures might exist!

The most famous of all water creatures are the lake monsters. Most countries have one. Scotland has Nessie, the monster in Loch Ness. Lake monsters from Canada include Ogopogo – long, slim and snake-like with a whiskery, horse-like head in Okanagan Lake, British Columbia. Yuk, seen around the King Islands, BC, usually only pokes its snake-like head and tail flipper out of the water.

Others include Manipogo in Lake Manitoba and Champ, also snake-like with the head of a horse, in Lake Champlain. In Lake Erie, on the Canada-USA border, you might see Bessie – a snake-like creature 9-15 m (30-50 ft) long.

The American Tessie lives in Lake Tahoe, on the California-Nevada border. It has its own museum with a telephone hotline for people to report sightings of it!

PING-FENG IS A CHINESE WATER MONSTER THAT LOOKS LIKE A BLACK PIG.

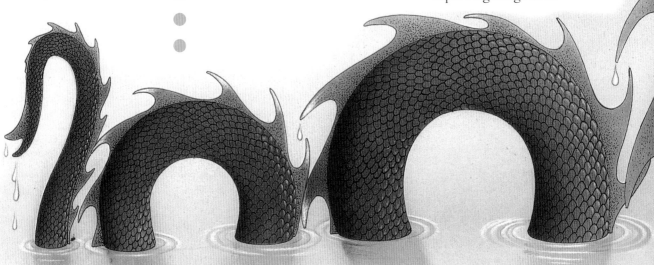

China has Chan, a giant vapour-breathing monster that lives in a lake in a deep gorge in a wild mountainous area. Fishermen throwing dynamite into the lake to kill fish were chased by an annoyed Chan.

Lake Kos Kol, in Kazakhstan, also has a Loch Ness-type monster living in it.

In Patagonia, Argentina, Nahuelitho lives in the 824 km squared (318 square miles) Nahuel Huapi Lake in the Andes mountains. Many years ago the local Indians told tales of a giant water animal and in 1922, scientists launched a search for a Patagonian plesiosaur (a dinosaur-like creature) after huge tracks were found around the edge of the lake.

At the end of 1995, Turkish investigators went to the country's largest lake, Lake Van, to look for another 'Nessie'. Reports say it was black and looked like a dinosaur with spikes on its back.

DEATHLY PUZZLE

In March 1969, the carcass of a strange sea creature was found on the beach in Tecoluta, Mexico. It weighed 36 tonnes (35 tons) and was covered in hard, jointed armour. Most puzzling of all was a tusk of bone 3m (10 ft) long, protruding from its head. A seven-man team of scientists commissioned to study the carcass decided it may be a finback whale, but this still did not explain the huge tusk. Biologists who saw the carcass said they 'could not match it with any sea creature known to man.'

River Dragon's Pearl

All Chinese dragons have a magic pearl, a gem of great power, which they keep hidden, usually in the fold of their leathery chins or in the mud at the bottom of their lake or river. Anything the dragon touches with its pearl grows and multiplies. Once, long ago, a poor Chinese boy planted some vegetable seeds in the river meadow where the grass was always lush and thick. As he dug he found a glowing ball. It was the river dragon's pearl. From then on, his fortune changed!

Lamia

Once a beautiful Libyan queen called Lamia was loved by the god Jupiter and bore him children. The jealous goddess Juno stole the children. As Lamia could not harm the goddess, she turned herself into a serpent-woman and vowed to kill and eat any human child she came across. Since then it was thought that many lamias, descended from that first Lamia, lived in the deserts of Africa where the whistling sound they made lured travellers to their death.

Serpents

IN MANY RELIGIONS, serpents, or snakes, were worshipped as gods or used as symbols. Because they shed their skin and emerged with a new one, snakes were seen as symbols of new life and resurrection. In Christianity, the snake is mostly linked to the devil and death, although Moses, when his people were struck by a plague in the desert, lifted up a brass snake that had the power to heal all those who looked at it.

When one of the Hydra's heads was cut off, two more were said to grow in its place.

A COILED SNAKE, with its tail in its mouth, forms a circle and so was often taken as a symbol for eternity – endless and limitless time. In old Norse legend, the Midgard serpent was thrown into the sea by Odin, where it grew so large it could encircle the Earth and bite its own tail.

BOAS WAS AN ENORMOUS SERPENT THAT LIVED IN ITALY IN AD 1.

It was often thought that the serpent's thrashing in the sea caused storms.

In Hindu mythology, the god Vishnu rides a cobra and sleeps on the coiled serpent of Earth's waters. The Celts linked the serpent to healing waters. The Hydra was a many-headed serpent that lived in a swamp near the well of Amymone, in the country of Argos. If one of the heads of the Hydra was cut off, two or more grew in its place.

ECHIDNA WAS THE HALF SERPENT MOTHER OF THE HYDRA IN GREEK MYTHOLOGY.

The head at the centre was immortal and one of the impossible tasks given to the Greek hero Hercules was to destroy the Hydra. He managed to burn away the side heads and buried the centre head under a rock.

The Aido Hwendo was a giant rainbow serpent from ancient African mythology, which carried the creator goddess Mawn as she created the universe. She coiled beneath the Earth to support its weight. It was thought that when Aido Hwendo changed position, she caused an earthquake.

AMPHISBAENA WAS A MEDIEVAL SERPENT WITH A HEAD AT EACH END OF ITS BODY.

For the Aborigines in Australia, the giant rainbow serpent in their mythology created life but in China and Africa, the serpent was seen as a rainmaker and the rainbow serpent as a thirst-quenching god. Native Americans also link the snake with rainmaking and have rainmaking dances in which they imitate the movements of a snake.

Ancient Greek and Roman altars often had a serpent carved on them and pet snakes were kept to guard the home. One Roman guardian serpent was called a 'genius'.

Quetzalcoatl is one of the oldest and most important gods and rulers of ancient Mexico. He was the Toltect god of learning, knowledge, air, holiness and self-sacrifice, and was known as the feathered serpent god – the plumed serpent. He went to the underworld to collect bones, which he sprinkled with his own blood to make the human race.

Medusa

In Greek mythology, Medusa was a mortal woman who became one of the three Gorgons – terrible female monsters with wings, claws and enormous teeth. Medusa's hair was a mass of writhing snakes and one glance at her face turned an onlooker to stone. She was killed by the hero Perseus, who cleverly avoided looking directly at her by using his shield as a mirror.

The Lambton Worm

During the Middle Ages, it was considered unlucky to fish on a Sunday. Young John Lambton did just that and caught a strange worm in the River Wear, UK, which he threw into a well and forgot about. Years later, when Lambton was a knight fighting in the crusades, the worm had grown into an enormous serpent that terrorised the countryside. When Sir Lambton returned from the Holy Land, he killed the worm and restored the peace.

WHOA BOA!

On 19 August 1991, a black serpent, probably a boa constrictor, estimated to be the length of two passenger buses 40 m (130 ft) long and 4.6 m (15 ft) in diameter, crashed through the jungle undergrowth and terrified the villages of Nevo Tacna, Peru. Reports on Peru's two national radio stations said the serpent had left a deep track wide enough to drive a tractor through, knocking down every tree in its path through the jungle and the village, before slipping into the River Napo. The incident was first reported by Jorge Chovez, Mayor of Mainas, 274 km (170 miles) north-east of Lima.

Chimera

The chimera is a female, fire-spewing monster from Greek mythology. It has a lion's body, a goat's head and a dragon's tail. The chimera is often used to symbolise the impossible. The Greek hero Bellerophon killed the chimera with the help of the goddess Minerva and the winged horse Pegasus.

Salamander

In the Middle Ages, a salamander was a lizard-like spirit that could live in fire unharmed; its body was so cold it quenched the heat of the fire. King Francis I of France had a lizard surrounded by flames on his badge design with the words 'Nutrisco et extinguo', which means 'I nourish and extinguish'. Alchemists (early chemists) were rumoured to use salamanders as temperature gauges when heating fire to turn lead into gold. When the fire was hot enough, the salamander leapt into the flames!

Cockatrice

The cockatrice and the basilisk both have the upper body of a rooster, the lower body of a snake and are supposedly hatched from a cock's egg. Just one glance from a cockatrice was said to kill. Its bite and the touch of its tail were so poisonous that once, when a rider on a horse killed a basilisk with a spear, the creature's venom rose through the spear and killed both horse and rider.

Fabulous beasts

MYTHS AND LEGENDS are full of fabulous creatures, many of which had power over aspects of life or provided tests for heroes. The creatures represented many different ideas from sacred truths and the power of the forces of nature, to birth, death and rebirth and the triumph of good over evil.

THE GRIFFIN was one of the noblest of the fabulous beasts. Made from two symbolically royal animals, it had the ears, body, hind legs and tail of a lion and the head, forefeet and wings of an eagle. The griffin combined knowledge, wisdom, strength and honour.

THE GRIFFIN WAS KNOWN TO THE SUMERIANS BY THE NAME OF CHAMBABA.

It was the link between man and the gods, being both beast and bird, of heaven and of Earth.

Stronger than eight lions and 100 eagles, the griffin was so big it was said to block the sun when flying. Sometimes called 'Hounds of Zeus', griffins were good guardians, showing gentleness if guarding humans from harm, but fierce protectiveness when guarding treasure.

Griffins were said to build nests near buried treasure. They were always at war with a race of one-eyed Sythian people, the Arimaspians, who were forever trying to steal their treasure.

The griffin seems to have originated in Middle Eastern legends. The earliest known picture of one is a carved marking found in what is now Iran and dates back to around 3000 BC.

In 7 BC, the Greek writer Aristeas described griffins that lived in a mountain range that could be the Urals or the Altai. By AD 14, griffins were shown in Roman folklore drawings.

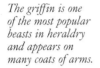

The griffin is one of the most popular beasts in heraldry and appears on many coats of arms.

Kappa

The Kappa lives in rivers in Japan and is harmless if treated politely. It has the head of a monkey and the legs of a frog. On the top of its head is a depression filled with water, which gives the Kappa its strength. If a Kappa attacks, the best way to defeat it is to bow, causing it to bow in response and so tip out the water on his head. It will then have to go back into the river for more. To avoid such meetings, carve your name on a cucumber and throw it into the river – the Kappa will then spare you!

The Greek god Apollo also rode a griffin and they later became a common symbol in heraldry.

In legend, griffins also symbolised arrogant pride. This was because Alexander the Great once tried to ride on one to the edge of the sky.

Nemesis, the goddess of retribution, took the form of a griffin at times and it was a griffin that turned her wheel of fortune. In ancient Roman art, griffins drew the chariot of Nemesis. They were seen as avenging beasts, relentlessly pursuing anyone who upset them.

GRIFFINS BUILT
NESTS AND LAID EGGS MADE OF
AGATE, A GEMSTONE.

QUESTING BEAST

In British folklore, the questing beast is an animal with a serpent's head, a leopard's body and the hooves of a deer. It was also known as the 'Beast Glatisant'. The cry of the questing beast was said to be like the baying of 60 hounds and terrible to hear. In the tales of King Arthur and his knights of the Round Table, King Arthur first saw the beast in a dream. In the dream the only time the beast was quiet was when it was drinking. One of the knights, Pellinore, spent his life chasing the questing beast and at his death, the Saracen knight, Palomides, took over the quest.

The Cyclopes

At the time when the heroes of old were returning to Greece after the Fall of Troy, the island of Sicily was believed to be inhabited by one-eyed giants, called Cyclopes. These giants had one enormous eye in the middle of their forehead. They were skilful shepherds who herded vast flocks of sheep on the mountains. Cyclopes fed on the flesh of sheep – and any people they could catch!

Werewolves

In Europe, in the late Middle Ages many men and some women were accused and convicted of being werewolves – humans who turned into hungry wolves at night. In France, between 1520 and 1630, more than 30,000 people were put on trial accused of being werewolves.

Genie

In Middle Eastern and Islamic folklore, a genie, or jinni, is a spirit made of fire or air, which can take on the form of a human or an animal. Genie are mischievous creatures who enjoy annoying humans, which is why they are often blamed for accidents.

Satyrs and friends

MANY CREATURES of mythology belong neither entirely to the animal kingdom nor to the world of humans, being part man and part beast. Some of the most famous of these creatures were the satyrs, men with the horns, ears and hindquarters of a goat. Generally they were seen as mischievous and idle, preferring to enjoy themselves rather than doing anything useful.

SATYRS WANDERED the wild places of the countryside. Companions of Dionysus, the god of wine, they spent their time drinking and dancing. The Romans called them fauns.

Pan was a satyr. He was the god of the woods, fields, flocks and shepherds. A keen musician, he invented a reed pipe, called the 'syrinx' or 'pan pipes'. This happened when he was chasing a wood spirit, or nymph, called Syrinx. She changed herself into a bed of reeds to escape Pan, and he pulled up the reeds and played a tune on them. From then on, he would play his pipe while the other nymphs danced.

Pan dwelt in caves and dark places and walked softly in the wood at night. The sound of his distant music or his sudden appearance often frightened travellers, and so the word 'panic' came to mean a sudden fright or terror without any visible cause.

PAN, THE SON OF HERMES, WAS MESSENGER OF THE GODS AND A NYMPH.

Satyrs are gods of the forest. They include pans, sylvans and fauns.

He was also seen as the protector of cattle and was often pictured holding a goblet and wearing a wolf skin. This is probably because the Romans also sometimes called him Lupercus, which means 'he who wards off the wolf'.

In Roman mythology, Faunus became the king of Latium in southern Italy.

He was the son of Picus, the Roman god of agriculture, and the grandson of the god Saturn. His partner was Fauna, the Roman earth mother and fertility goddess. On 15 February each year, the people of ancient Rome celebrated the Festival of Lupercalia, to honour the god Faunus. During the festival the priests of Lupercus, called Luperci, dressed in goatskins and walked through the streets of Rome amid pagan celebration.

His name also means 'all' and eventually Pan came to be seen as a symbol of the whole world of nature.

Faunus was the Roman god of wild nature and, like the satyrs, his favourite occupation was drinking and dancing.

Were-Jaguars

The ancient Olmecs and Mayans believed that were-jaguars, beasts with the head, body and tail of a jaguar and the legs of a man, came from the supernatural world to prey on humans or teach them lessons. In Mayan mythology, four giant jaguar gods held up the sky, a white one at the north corner, a yellow one at the south corner, red at the east and black at the west.

Sirens

The sirens were water creatures from ancient Greek legends. Half woman, half bird, they sang enchanting songs to lure sailors to their doom on the rocks and reefs. In ancient Greek mythology, the hero Odysseus escaped from the sirens by plugging the ears of his crew so they could not hear the songs and by having himself tied to the ship's mast so he could not follow their haunting sounds.

MINOTAUR

In ancient Greek mythology, the Minotaur was the child of Queen Pasiphae of Crete, Greece, and was a man with the head of a bull. His father Minos kept him imprisoned in an underground maze that was so complicated, no one could find their way out. The Minotaur ate only human flesh, so Minos had arranged with the King of Athens that every nine years, seven girls and seven boys were sent underground for it to eat. One year, Theseus, the king's son was one of the chosen children. With the help of Minos's daughter, who gave him a ball of string to track his way round the maze, Theseus killed the Minotaur and put an end to the human sacrifice.

Weird and Wonderful

WHILE MOST PREHISTORIC creatures are long gone, some are still with us. Snow fleas, some spiders, snails, cockroaches and the horseshoe crab have remained unchanged for millions of years. Also on our planet are many creatures that to our eyes look odd yet they are living evidence of the wonderful variety of nature.

Cassowary

This large, black-feathered, flightless bird is the only bird in the world to have armour. It has a grey, bony 'helmet' on its blue-skinned head.

Opossum

Nicknamed 'Old Slowpoke', the opossum's favourite trick is pretending to be dead if attacked. This act is so convincing that a pack of hounds has even been seen to give up and go away, leaving the opossum to get up and wander off.

Coelacanth

In 1938, a trawler fishing off the coast of Africa caught a very odd-looking fish. It was about 1.5 m (5 ft) long, steel-blue and covered in heavy scales. Until then scientists thought the coelacanth has died out more than 65 million years ago.

Aardvark

Its name meaning 'earth-pig' in African, this hump-backed, rabbit-eared, long-snouted animal feeds on ants and termites in many parts of Africa. Unlike the anteater, which is toothless, the aardvark has 20 rootless teeth which grow continually throughout its life.

Okapi

The okapi lives in the tropical forests of Central Africa. It has the legs of a zebra, the body of an antelope and moves like a giraffe with the high speed of an ostrich. It also has four stomachs, eyes that can look in different directions simultaneously and a transparent tongue 35 cm (14 in) long.

Duck-billed platypus

When scientists were first presented with the dead body of a duck-billed platypus, they thought someone was playing a joke on them. It looked as if bits of other animals had been stuck together. An egg-laying mammal that is at home in the water, the platypus is covered in fur with a beaver-like tail, has webbed feet and the beak of a duck. This oddity of nature has survived on the planet for 50 million years.

Tapir

A tapir looks as if it can't make up its mind whether it wants to be a pig, an elephant or a rhinoceros. As a hoofed animal, it walks on its toes. However, its feet are unusual in that although each front foot has four toes, the hind feet have only three. A tapir can hide underwater using its trunk as a snorkel.

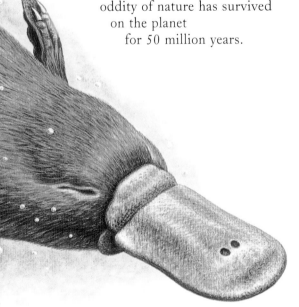

When diving underwater the duck-billed platypus uses its sensitive bill to probe for food.

Extinct animals

EVERYONE KNOWS that dinosaurs are long gone and that dodos are dead, but did you know that around 100 animal species become extinct every single day? Many more species will soon be extinct because there are too few of them for the species to survive for long, no matter what we do. Many animals, particularly smaller species of insects and sponges, are becoming extinct before we have even studied them.

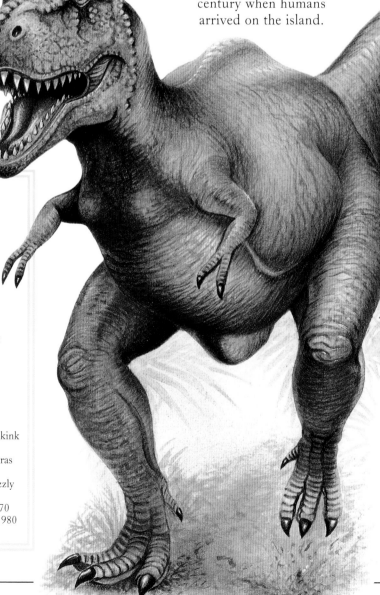

Dodo

The slow and clumsy, flightless dodo birds lived on Mauritius and Reunion Islands in the Indian Ocean. They became extinct in the 18th century when humans arrived on the island.

Dinosaurs

Around 200 million years ago dinosaurs appeared on Earth. They roamed the planet for 140 million years and then suddenly died out. Many scientists believe that a giant meteor crashed into the sea and caused a change in the climate that killed off the dinosaurs.

Extinct animals

Extinct means that the last living individual of a species has died or been killed and that species has vanished from the Earth forever. Extinctions are gathering pace and since the 1990s at least one species probably disappears every day. Still more species are on the slippery slope towards extinction unless we change what we are doing to animals, their habitats and the planet on which we all live. Some extinct animals are:

- Dodo 1770
- Arizona Jaguar 1905
- Huia 1907
- Passenger Pigeon 1914
- Florida Black Wolf 1917
- Kamchutka Bear 1920
- Tasmanian Wolf 1933
- Bali Tiger 1937
- Leopard Frog 1930s
- Cape Verde Giant Skink 1940
- Lake Titicaca Orestras 1950
- Mexican Silver Grizzly Bear 1967
- Texas Red Wolf 1970
- Round Island Boa 1980

Huia

The huia birds lived in the forests of New Zealand's North Island. People hunted them and destroyed their forest habitat. By 1907, the species had been killed off.

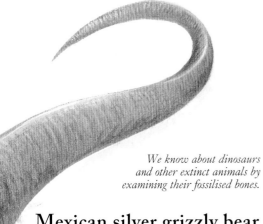

We know about dinosaurs and other extinct animals by examining their fossilised bones.

Mexican silver grizzly bear

Known as 'the silver one', this bear was hunted until there were no more alive. In 1960 there were only 30 left in the world, but still ranchers killed them until, by 1967, they had all disappeared.

Lake Titicaca orestra

Orestras were unique fish that lived only in Lake Titicaca, which straddles Peru and Bolivia. They preferred shallow water and never left the lake to explore the rivers. In 1937, lake trout was put into the water. The trout ate many of the smaller creatures in the lake, including the young orestras. By 1950 there were no orestras left.

Passenger pigeon

At one time, passenger pigeons covered much of eastern North America, living in the trees across the land. Out of every 10 birds in North America, four were passenger pigeons. They were once the most numerous birds in existence. Between 1860 and 1900, humans hunted and killed all of them except one, Martha. Martha spent the last 14 years of her life in Cincinnati Zoo, USA, where she died in 1914.

Florida black wolf

From Florida to Georgia, Alabama and Tennessee, the black wolf roamed the swamps, forests, plains and hills of the USA in great numbers. Then in the 1800s humans began to settle on the land, chopping down trees, building houses, farming the land and eating the wildlife. Huge numbers of black wolves starved to death. Those that were left were shot, trapped or poisoned. By 1917 there were no more black wolves.

Endangered animals

AN ANIMAL SPECIES IS ENDANGERED when the number of individuals alive falls so low they may not be able to bear enough young to continue their species. Species become endangered for many reasons. Sometimes animals are killed by humans. Animals also die because their habitats are destroyed and they lose their homes or food supplies. Today, over 7,000 species are at risk of extinction.

Gorillas

Gorillas are killed for different parts of their bodies, which are used in medicine or sold as souvenirs to tourists. Sometimes young gorillas are sold to zoos. Often their forest homes are cleared for the wood or the land for farming.

Bears

Bears are endangered because of the way that humans treat them. They are caught and kept in cages too small for them and their bile is taken for Chinese medicine. Others are used as dancing or fighting bears for the tourist trade.

Manatees

The slow-moving, large-eyed manatees live and swim in the coastal seas and waterways where humans also play and hunt. The Many of their deaths are human-related. The manatee is a gentle creature who cradles her young in her arms.

Conservation

Conservation is a way of preserving the planet and its life forms by setting aside areas of land and sea where the habitats and the animals that live in them are protected. Only a very small percentage of the world's land surface and its wild spaces are protected in this way. Agreements between countries, such as CITES (Convention on International Trade in Endangered Species) also help to protect animals.

Zoos

Zoos are places where wild animals are kept in captivity – often species of which there are only a few left, so that they can breed in safety. Some zoos run education programmes to teach people how to protect species.

Reserves

Reserves are areas of land or water where wild animals are protected from being hunted and can live and breed in safety. The world's first reserve was the Yellowstone National Park in Wyoming, USA.

Things you can do to help:

Try one or all of these suggestions to help preserve the Earth's endangered species.

1) Join one of the organisations listed at the back of this book.
2) Refuse to buy products that contain animal ingredients such as fur, ivory and tortoiseshell.
3) Refuse to buy products that have been tested on animals.
4) Think about what you eat.
5) Start or join a local community effort to save an area of land used by wildlife.
6) Buy recycled paper and save paper for recycling to help conserve forested habitats.
7) Make a mini-wildlife reserve in your back garden or at your school.
8) Refuse to buy pets, such as parrots, that have been caught in the wild and transported to your country.
9) Learn as much as you can about how animals become endangered and find out more ways in which to help them.

Black Rhino

The black rhino is an African rhino, killed mainly for its horn. The horn is powdered and used in oriental medicines, or carved into dagger handles in the Middle East. Rhino horn trade has been banned worldwide for over 20 years but illegal trade continues. Rhino numbers have dropped 95 percent since 1970.

Glossary

ACCELERATE To increase the speed of motion.

ALIEN A being or thing foreign to its environment.

ALTITUDE The height of the land.

AMNESIA Memory-loss.

ANCIENT EGYPT The time when Egypt was ruled by the pharaohs between 3100 BC and 30 BC.

ANCIENT GREECE The time when the Greeks set up a society that became the most influential in the world from 1500 BC to 323 BC.

ANCIENT ROME The time when the Roman Empire ruled western Europe, the Middle East, and the north coast of Africa from 753 BC to AD 476.

ANTARCTIC The continent around the South Pole and the surrounding waters where average temperatures are below freezing.

ANTENNAE A pair of mobile feelers on the heads of insects, crustaceans etc, that often respond to touch and taste.

AQUATIC Living, growing or found in water.

BACTERIA A large group of micro-organisms many of which cause disease.

BEAST OF BURDEN An animal such as a horse, donkey or ox used for carrying loads.

BILL The projecting jaws of a bird covered with a horny sheath.

BIOSPHERE The part of the Earth's surface and atmosphere inhabited by living things.

BIRD Any warm-blooded egg-laying vertebrate with a body covering of feathers and wings.

CAMOUFLAGE The means by which animals escape the notice of predators.

CAPTIVITY Imprisonment.

CARCASS The dead body of an animal.

CARNIVORE Any animal or plant that feeds on animals.

CHRISTIAN Religion relating to Jesus Christ, his teachings, example or followers.

CHRYSALIS The pupa of a moth or butterfly, in a case or cocoon.

CLASSICAL Relating to the ancient Greeks and Romans or their civilisation.

CLIMATE The long-term weather conditions of an area.

COCOON A silky protective envelope made by silkworms and certain insect larvae in which the pupae develop.

COLONY A group of the same type of animal or plant living or growing together.

COMMUNITY A group of interdependent plants and animals inhabiting the same region.

COMPOUND EYE The eye of some insects and some crustaceans which consists of many separate light-sensitive units.

CONSERVATION The protection, preservation and careful management of natural resources.

CONSTELLATION Any of the groups of stars as seen from Earth. Many were named by the ancient Greeks after animals or mythological persons.

CORRAL An enclosure for cattle or horses.

CRUSTACEAN Any aquatic invertebrate, such as crabs and lobsters, having jointed limbs, a segmented body and an outer-skeleton made of chitin.

CUB The young of certain animals such as foxes, wolves, lions and bears.

CUD Partially digested food regurgitated from the first stomach to the mouth to be chewed again.

CULTIVATE To plant, tend or harvest.

CULTURE The inherited ideas, beliefs, values and knowledge of a particular society.

DESCENDANT Something that derives from an earlier form.

DISCIPLE A follower of a teacher or a school of thought.

DOMESTIC Bred or kept by humans as a pet or for the supply of food.

DOMINANT Having authority or influence.

ECHOLOCATION Finding the position of an object by bouncing sound off it and measuring the time it takes.

ELONGATED Extra long or extended.

EMBLEM A badge or picture symbol.

EMPATHY A deep understanding for another person's or animal's feelings.

ENDANGERED In danger of extinction.

ENVIRONMENT The surroundings in which an animal lives that influence its development and behaviour.

EQUALITY Being equal.

ESTIMATE To calculate roughly.

EVOLUTION The gradual change in the characteristics of a population of animals or plants over many generations.

EXTINCT Having died out.

FIELD OF VISION The area that the eye is able to see without having to turn the head.

FLOCK A group of animals of one kind especially sheep or birds.

FOOD CHAIN A series of organisms in a community each of which feeds on another in the chain and is in turn eaten.

FOSSIL A relic of a plant or animal that existed in a past age in the form of mineralised bones and shells.

FRESHWATER Of or living in fresh water.

GENETICS The study of heredity and variation in plants and animals.

GLOBAL WARMING An increase in the average temperature worldwide believed to be caused by the greenhouse effect.

GRAZE To feed on the plants of a patch of land.

GREENHOUSE EFFECT The warming up of the Earth due to human-made carbon dioxide in the atmosphere that traps the Sun's heat near the surface of the Earth.

HABITAT The natural home of an animal.

HARNESS The arrangement of straps fitted to an animal so that the animal can pull a cart

HERBIVORE An animal that feeds on grass and other plants.

HERD A large group of mammals living and feeding together.

HIBERNATE To pass the winter in a dormant condition.

HINDU Relating to the beliefs and customs which form the main religion of India.

HIVE A natural or artificial structure for housing a colony of bees

HYPOTHERMIA An extremely low body temperature caused by exposure to cold

IMMATURE Not fully grown or developed.

IMMORTAL Does not die or decay.

IMMUNE Protected from infection or danger.

INCUBATE To supply eggs with heat to help them hatch.

INSTINCT The behavioural reactions that an animal is born with and does not have to learn.

INVERTEBRATE Any animal lacking a backbone.

JEWISH Characteristic of the religion of the Jews, based on the Old Testament and having a central belief in one God.

KIN A class or group with similar characteristics.

LARVAE Young of many animals that develop into a different adult form by metamorphosis.

LATIUM An ancient territory in Italy inhabited by Latin people from 10 BC to 4 BC

LEGEND A popular story passed on from earlier times whose truth has not been confirmed.

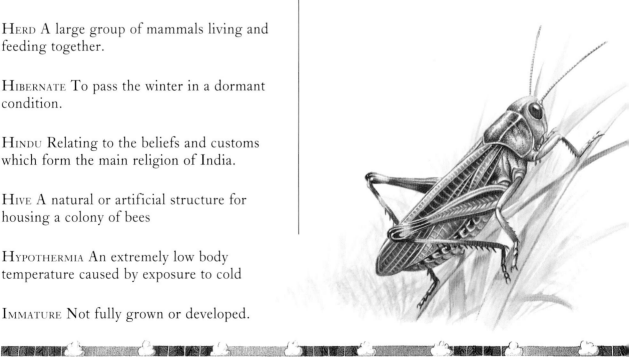

LIFE CYCLE The series of changes in the life of an animal between one stage and the identical stage in the next generation.

LOTUS A water plant with large leaves, a beautiful perfume and pinkish flowers, regarded as sacred in ancient Egypt.

MAMMAL Any warm-blooded vertebrate which feeds its milk to its young.

MEMBRANE A thin layer of tissue that covers or connects inner parts of an animal's body.

MIDDLE AGES The period from about AD 1000 to the 15th century.

MIGRATE To journey between specific habitats at specific times of the year.

MIMIC To imitate or copy.

MUSLIM Relating to the ideas and culture of Islamic religion.

MUZZLE The projecting part of the head, usually the jaws and nose of animals such as the horse and dog.

MYTH A story about superhuman beings of an earlier age.

MYXOMATOSIS A highly infectious, usually fatal disease of rabbits.

NATIVE Born in a specified place.

NATIVE AMERICAN A person who belongs to the race of original inhabitants of America, as distinguished from invaders or settlers.

NAVIGATE To direct oneself carefully or safely.

NOCTURNAL Being active at night

NORSE Coming from Norway.

OPPORTUNIST A person or animal that seizes opportunities when available.

OPPOSABLE THUMB A thumb that can be placed opposite the other fingers so it can touch the ends of each.

ORAL Spoken as opposed to written form of communication.

ORPHANAGE A home for the protection of abandoned children or animals.

PACK A group of animals of the same kind.

PACKHORSE Horse used to transport goods and equipment for humans.

PAGAN Word used to describe the ancient religion based on respect for all life, or the follower of that religion.

PARADOX A person or thing exhibiting apparently contradictory characteristics.

PARASITE An animal that feeds off another

PERSECUTE To oppress, harass or treat badly.

POLLINATE To transfer the pollen produced by one part of a seed-bearing plant to allow it to reproduce.

POLLUTION Poisonous or harmful substances.

POPULATION A group of individuals of the same species inhabiting a given area.

POROUS Lets through air, water or other fluids.

PREDATOR A meat-eating animal.

PREDICT To make known in advance.

PREHISTORIC Relating to a time before written records were made.

PREVAIL To prove superior.

PRIDE A group of lions.

PRIMATE A mammal, including apes and humans, with flexible hands, good eyesight and a highly developed brain.

PROSPERITY The condition of being successful.

PROVOKE To anger.

PTERODACTYL An extinct flying reptile.

PUPA The inactive non-feeding stage of development of some insects between the larval and adult stages when many internal changes occur.

PUPATE To develop into a pupa.

PURIFY To make clean.

RARE Not widely distributed.

RECYCLE To reclaim or pass through a system for further use.

REGURGITATE To bring back into the mouth after swallowing.

REPTILE Cold-blooded vertebrates, such as tortoises, snakes, lizards and crocodiles, characterised by lungs, an outer covering of horny scale or plates, and young produced in eggs.

RUDDER Anything that guides or directs.

RUMP The hindquarters of an animal, not including the legs.

SCAVENGER Any animal that feeds on decaying flesh.

SCENT A smell given off by an animal.

SECRETION A substance released from a plant or animal cell.

SHED To cast off or lose.

SIGN LANGUAGE The visual communication of symbols made with the hands.

SOLITARY Living alone.

SPECIES A group of animals that are capable of interbreeding and share common attributes.

STABILISER Any device that makes something steady.

STEALTHY Secretive, unobserved.

SUBCONSCIOUS The part of the mind on the edge of consciousness.

SUPERSTITION Irrational belief especially regarding the unknown.

SURPLUS A quantity or amount extra to what is needed.

SYMBOL Something that represents or stands for something else.

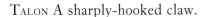

TALON A sharply-hooked claw.

TAME Changed by humans from a wild state into a domesticated condition.

TECHNOLOGY The practical use of science and knowledge.

TERRITORY An area inhabited and defended by an animal or a group of animals.

TICKS Blood-sucking parasites.

TIGRESS A female tiger.

TRANCE A dazed state resembling sleep.

VENOM A poisonous fluid secreted by animals such as snakes.

VERTEBRATES An animal with a bony skeleton and a well-developed brain including fish, amphibians, reptiles, birds and mammals.

VULNERABLE Capable of being damaged or destroyed.

WARM-BLOODED Having a constant body temperature usually higher than the surrounding environment.

WATERFOWL Any aquatic freshwater bird.

WILD Not domesticated or tame.

WILDLIFE RESERVE A protected area of land or water where animals can live in as natural a state as possible.

WORSHIP To be devoted to and full of admiration for.

WRATH Anger.

ZOO Place where living animals are kept, studied, bred and exhibited to the public.

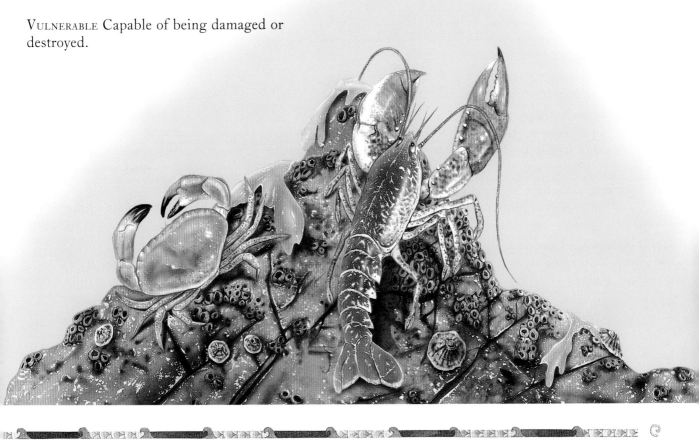

Index

Useful addresses

When writing to these societies please remember to enclose a stamped, addressed envelope. Many of these groups have a junior club or newsletter and will send you lots of useful information.

COMPASSION IN WORLD FARMING
Salmon Weir
Hanover St
Cork
Ireland
Tel: 00 353 21 427 2441
Fax: 00 353 21 427 4984

ROYAL SOCIETY FOR THE
PROTECTION OF BIRDS
The Lodge
Sandy, Bedfordshire
SG19 2DL
UK
Tel: 01767 680551

WORLD SOCIETY FOR THE
PROTECTION OF ANIMALS
89 Albert Embankment
London
SE1 7TP
UK
Tel: 020 7587 5000
Fax: 020 7793 0208

INTERNATIONAL DOLPHIN
WATCH
10 Melton Rd
North Ferriby
East Yorkshire
HU14 3ET, UK
Tel: 01482 632850
Fax: 01482 634914

ANIMAL AID
The Old Chapel
Bradford St
Tonbridge
Kent
TN9 1AW
UK
Tel: 01732 364546
Fax: 01732 366533

BRITISH HEDGEHOG PRESERVATION
SOCIETY
Hedgehog House
Dhustone
Ludlow
Shropshire
SY8 3PL
UK
Tel: 01584 890801

LEAGUE AGAINST CRUEL SPORTS LTD
83/87 Union St
London
SE1 1SG
UK
Tel: 020 7403 6155
Fax: 020 7403 4532

WHALE AND DOLPHIN CONSERVATION
SOCIETY
P.O. Box 232
Melksham
Wiltshire
SN12 7SB
UK
Tel: 01249 449500
Fax: 01249 449501

PEOPLE'S TRUST FOR ENDANGERED
SPECIES
15 Cloisters House
8 Battersea Park Rd
London
SW8 4BG
Tel: 020 7498 4533
Fax: 020 7498 4459

BORN FREE FOUNDATION
3 Grove House
Foundry Lane
Horsham
West Sussex
RH13 5PL
Tel: 01403 240170
Fax: 01403 327838

WILDFOWL AND WETLANDS TRUST
Slimbridge
Gloucester
GL2 7BT
UK
Tel: 01453 891900
Fax: 01453 890827

RSPCA
Wilberforce Way
Southwater
Horsham
West Sussex RH13 9RS
UK
Tel: 0870 3335999
Fax: 0870 7530284

WWF
Panda House
Weyside Park
Godalming
Surrey GU7 1XR
UK
Tel: 01483 426444
Fax: 01483 426409

FRIENDS OF THE EARTH
INTERNATIONAL
PO Box 19199
1000 GD Amsterdam
The Netherlands
Tel: +010 31 20 622 1369
Fax: +010 31 20 639 2181

GREENPEACE INTERNATIONAL
Ottho Heldringstraat 5
1066 AZ Amsterdam
The Netherlands
Tel: +010 31 20 523 222

WILDLIFE AFRICA CONSERVATION
129a Kitson St
Watervaal Estate
Northcliff
Johannesburg
South Africa
Tel: +27 11 7823410

NATURAL RESOURCES CONSERVATION
SERVICE
14th and Independence Avenue
Washington DC 20250
USA

CONSERVATION INTERNATIONAL
1919 M Street
NW Suite 600
Washington DC 20036
USA
Tel: 001 202 912 1000

RSPCA
20 Station Rd
South Norwood
London SE25 5AJ
UK

Acknowledgments

Abbreviations: t=top; b=bottom; c=centre; l=left; r=right;

Picture credits:
B. & C. Alexander/NHPA 10tr
A.N.T./NHPA 92tl
Anthony Bannister/NHPA 10lc, 67tr, 123tl
Henry Ausloos/NHPA 126bl, 127c
G. I. Bernard/NHPA 10br, 60bl, 82tl, 125tr
Joe Blossom/NHPA 70b
Ian Bradshaw/Telegraph Colour Library 42-43c
Laurie Campbell/NHPA 11tl, 124tr
Stephen Dalton/NHPA 54bl, 56bl, 66-67c
Susanne Danegger/NHPA 39tl
Nigel J. Dennis/NHPA 97c
European Space Agency/Science Photo Library 8tl
E Hanumantha Rao/NHPA 19t
Martin Harvey/NHPA 123br, 126b
Daniel Heuclin/NHPA 79tc, 122tr
E.A. Janes/NHPA 73t
B Jones and M Shimlock/NHPA 11bl, 74c, 83br
Rich Kirchner/NHPA 16b, 65bl
Stephen Krafemann/NHPA 14c
Gerard Lacz/NHPA 24-25, 123tr
Jay Pack Picture Library/Telegraph Colour Library 113tr
Haroldo Palo Jr/NHPA 8b, 8tr
NASA 43tr
Eero Murtomaki/NHPA 52c
David E Myers/NHPA 67c
National Gallery, London/Bridgeman Art Library 108tl
Pinacoteca Capitolina, Palazzo Conservatori, Rome/ The Bridgeman Art Library 31tr
Haroldo Palo Jr/NHPA 69c
Andy Rouse/NHPA 26-27t
Jany Sauvenet/NHPA 66bl, 122c
Kevin Schafer/NHPA 51tl, 52bl, 96b
John Shaw/NHPA 21, 10bl, 11br, 104c
Stephen Simpson/Telegraph Colour Library 37tc
Eric Sodor/NHPA 11tr, 121tr
H Sykes/Telegraph Colour Library 109b
Michael Tweedie/NHPA 80-81b
Hellio & Van Ingen/NHPA 59br
Martin Wendler/NHPA 81t
Peter Willi/Bridgeman Art Library 36bl

Bill Wood/NHPA 88tl
David Woodfall/NHPA 11rc, 64bl
Norbett Wu/NHPA 78tl, 122bl

Illustrations by:
Adam Abel 58-59c, 81br, 82-83bl, 109cr, 132tl
Craig Austin 50-51bl,-c, 76-77b, 78-79c
Alan Baker 49tr, 108-109c, 114-115c
John Barber 62-63c, 98c
Andy Beckett 19b, 38bl, 138tl
Leslet Betts 20t, 47tr
Lucy Bristow 70-71c
Wayne Ford 3c, 32b, 40b, 46-47c
Lena Fricher 36-37c
Roger Gorringe 54-55c, 90-91c
Darren Harvey 88-89c
Tim Hayward 126br
Martin Knowlden 48bl, 111tr, 116b, 118-119c, 128br, 143c
Josephine Martin 71tr, 94-95c
Danuta Mayer 34bl, 70tl, 119tr
Steve Noon 1c, 17b, 22-23c, 30-31c, 34-35c, 82-83c
Richard Orr 9, 12-13
Steve Roberts 53br, 10-11c, 84-85c, 92-93c, 124-125c, 131bl, 139br
Andrew Robinson 4b, 60-61c, 135br
Judy Stephens 42tl, 86tl, 88cl
Mark Stewart 72c, 136bl
Simon Turvey 6t, 102b, 122-123c
Unterliden Museum, Colmar, France 110b
Garry Walton 1t, 3t, 106-107c, 107tr, 111cr, 112-113c, 120bl,
Andrew Wheatcroft 40-41c, 120-121c
Nadine Wickenden borders throughout the book.
Sarah Young 4t, 23tr, 60tl, 99tr, 114tl, 118tl, 120tl
Dover Books for all black and white illustrations
Panda device ƒ 1986 WWF – World Wide Fund for Nature 22t

Please note that every effort has been made to trace copyright holders. Alligator Books apologises in advance for any unintentional omissions and would be glad to include an appropriate acknowledgement in subsequent editions of this publication.